The
Realm
of
Science

DIRECTIONS AND
DIMENSIONS OF
LIFE: Ecology,
Man and Nature

VOLUME 20

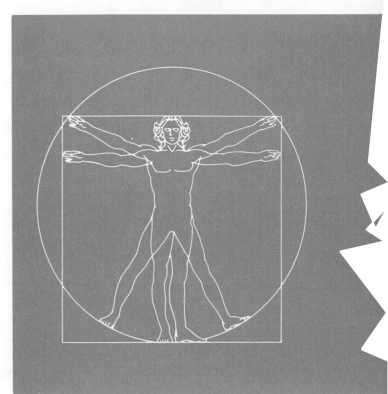

THE
REALM
OF
SCIENCE

DAVID ROSENBERG, *Director*

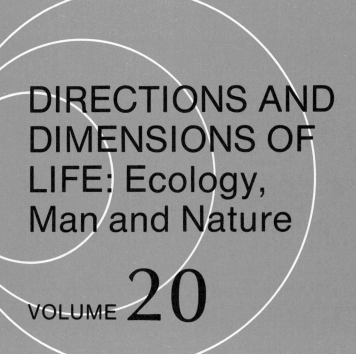

DIRECTIONS AND DIMENSIONS OF LIFE: Ecology, Man and Nature

VOLUME 20

STANLEY B. BROWN Editor-in-Chief

L. BARBARA BROWN Associate Editor

TOUCHSTONE PUBLISHING COMPANY   *Louisville, Kentucky*

Human history
becomes more and more
a race
between education
and catastrophe.

H. G. WELLS

THE REALM OF SCIENCE is divided into 5 parts, each covering a broad concept of science rather than a traditional discipline.

CONTENTS

CONSULTANTS AND CONTRIBUTORS

LAWRENCE H. BALTHASER
Department of Physical Sciences
California State Polytechnic College
San Luis Obispo, California

ROBERT BLAKELY
Indiana Geological Survey
Indiana University
Bloomington, Indiana

RICHARD BOOLOOTIAN
Department of Zoology
University of California
Los Angeles, California

JOSEPH C. BOONE
Department of Physical Sciences
California State Polytechnic College
San Luis Obispo, California

MARTIN S. BURKHEAD
Department of Astronomy
Indiana University
Bloomington, Indiana

LOUISE B. DUNN
Department of Anthropology
University of Utah
Salt Lake City, Utah

WILLIAM W. EIDSON
Department of Physics
University of Missouri at St. Louis
St. Louis, Missouri

LEO C. FAY
Department of Education
Indiana University
Bloomington, Indiana

DAVID W. HAFEMEISTER
Department of Physics
California State Polytechnic College
San Luis Obispo, California

CHARLES W. HAGEN, JR.
Department of Biology
Indiana University
Bloomington, Indiana

ELIZABETH O. HANSEN
Division of Science Education
University of California
Berkeley, California

JULIUS T. HANSEN
Department of Physiology
Medical School, St. Louis University
St. Louis, Missouri

VIRGIL HENISER
Coordinator for School Science
Indiana University
Bloomington, Indiana

CHRISTIAN E. KASLOW
Department of Chemistry
Indiana University
Bloomington, Indiana

BRUCE C. KETCHAM
Department of Aerospace, Office of Research
University of Tulsa
Tulsa, Oklahoma

PAUL E. KLINGE
Associate Dean, Research
Indiana University
Bloomington, Indiana

WENDELL F. McBURNEY
Science Coordinator
Indiana University
Bloomington, Indiana

LEO OLINER
Chief of Research in Endocrine
  and Metabolism
Veterans Administration Office
Washington, D. C.

THOMAS G. PERRY
Department of Geology
Indiana University
Bloomington, Indiana

JOHN RODGERS
Department of Philosophy
St. John's College
Santa Fe, New Mexico

JOHN H. RUGHEIMER
Department of Physics
Indiana University
Bloomington, Indiana

MILLARD SEELEY
Department of Chemistry
University of Arizona
Tuscon, Arizona

MAYNARD THOMPSON
Department of Mathematics
Indiana University
Bloomington, Indiana

JAMES A. WIXOM
Department of Mathematics
University of Utah
Salt Lake City, Utah

JANIS B. WIXOM
Churchill Junior High School
Salt Lake City, Utah

ARTHUR YOUNG
Department of Astronomy and Physics
San Diego State College
San Diego, California

EDITORIAL STAFF

Managing Editor: Richard E. Kirk
Senior Editor: Charlotte A. Jeanes
Coordinating Editor: Phyllis W. Kirk
Art Editor: Mary E. Holloway
Research Editor: Jean M. White
Contributing Editors: James N. Rogers
    Frances L. Hackett
Editorial Assistants: Della A. Sarks
    Joyce Walaszek
    Peggy Patrick
    Barbara Lind
    Ruth Harley

ART STAFF

Art Director: Ben J. Sandman
Designer: Joseph Yurkas

CONTRIBUTING ARTISTS:
Eric Wehder Jr.
Ralph A. Welch
Fred DeCore
Robert W. Weston
Robert B. Dempley
David E. Barned
Raymond L. Eckerle
David R. Williams
Charles J. Bauer
Louis E. Givan
James E. Summers
Enoch Harned

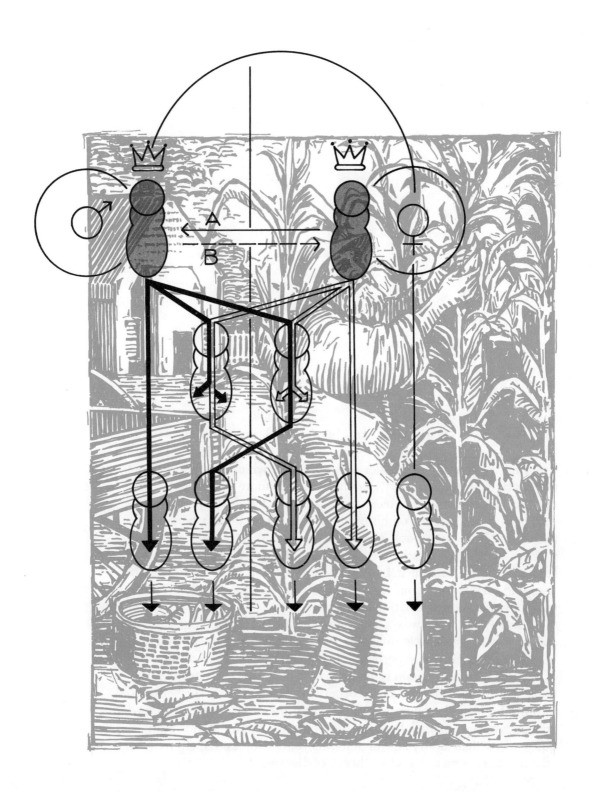

Man's CURIOSITY about himself and his world is ageless. The history of scientific endeavor records this curiosity. Every field of science shows an inherent order of observation which progressed from the relatively superficial and speculative to the more sophisticated and specific, as knowledge and techniques accumulated. Each man's observations rest, to a degree, on his predecessors'. From today's perspective it is possible to look back and identify certain key observations in various fields which contributed greatly to the consolidation of knowledge and established a firm basis for new expansion. The progression of scientific observation from the superficial to the sophisticated is illustrated in many of the selections that follow.

Athanasius Kircher was a German scholar and archeologist of the 1600s. His range of scientific observation and experimentation was vast. Here, in a famous experiment, he describes the apparent hypnosis of a hen. This phenomenon is well known today. But Kircher's observations did not include just easily observable phenomena. He ventured into the highly speculative by proposing in the late 1600s that disease and decay were caused by invisible bodies, a theory that would require more than 300 years of scientific endeavor and technological advance to emerge as the virus theory of disease.

On the Hypnosis of a Hen

From Athanasius Kircher, *Physiologia* (1674), translated by J. S. Kestlerus (1680), p. 90. Reprinted by permission of the publisher from *The History of Biology: An Introduction*, edited by F. S. Bodenheimer. Wm. Dawson & Sons Ltd., 1958, pp. 274-275.

LAY A hen bound on its feet on any floor. It will, at first feel as a captive and will try by all means—shaking of its wings and movements of its entire body—to free itself from its fetters. But finally it despairs of obtaining its freedom, grows quiet and puts itself at the disposal of the victor's judgment. When now the hen remains quiet, draw with chalk a straight line on the pavement, beginning from the hen's eyes, or draw there with any colour something on the pavement which resembles a rope, and then release the fetters of the hen. I say that whenever the hen is liberated from its fetters, it remains almost motionless, even if you goad it to fly away. There is no reason for this behaviour other than the very great imagination of the bird which takes the line drawn on the pavement for fetters by which it is bound.

There is no doubt, that this occurs also in other animals.

U NTIL THE MIDDLE of the 1700s, people believed that muscles were hollow and contained some mysterious spirit or fluid. One man who did not subscribe to this view was Albrecht von Haller, a Swiss anatomist and physiologist. Haller contributed many important ideas to medicine, including recognition of the mechanism of respiration and the automatism of the heart.

In the following article, Haller describes some of his work that demonstrated the nerve-muscle relationship. He was the first to demonstrate that sensibility and irritability are independent, the former being a property of tissues endowed with nerves, the latter a peculiarity of all muscular tissue, independent of the nerves proceeding to it, and surviving in severed parts.

Haller's conceptions of the nature of living substance and of the action of the nervous system have caused him to be called the founder of modern neurology.

On the Irritability of the Nerves

From Albrecht von Haller, *Dissertation sur les parties irritables et sensible des Animaux* (1755), p. 39. Reprinted by permission of the publisher from *The History of Biology: An Introduction*, edited by F. S. Bodenheimer. Wm. Dawson & Sons Ltd., 1958, pp. 307-308.

IRRITABILITY (read: contractility) is so different from sensibility, that the most irritable parts are not sensitive, and the most sensitive are not irritable. I shall also demonstrate, that irritability does not depend upon the nerves, but upon the primordial structure of the irritable parts.

The nerves, those organs of every sensation, have no irritability at all. This is astonishing, but true. When I irritate a nerve, the muscle which it innervates shows immediately convulsions. This is always the case, as I have often shown for the diaphragm and for the abdominal muscles of a rat, or for the leg muscles of a frog. . . . But when one irritates the nerves within these muscles, the nerves never show contraction, as I have ascertained often in dogs and frogs . . . I have (also) used a mathe-matical instrument divided into very small sections. This I laid along the nerve, which remained perfectly immobile during strong stimulation. This experiment, by the way, does not agree with the oscillations attributed often to nerves . . .

On cutting the crural nerve of a dog, its legs became insensitive; one may subject it to any kind of maltreatment and the animal will not show any sign of suffering. But when this cut nerve is stimulated, the muscles of the leg show convulsions . . .

I have also ligatured (lié) in small animals the nerve-trunks which go to the extremities. I thus paralysed the legs and made them insensitive. When I afterwards stimulated the muscles, they contracted as before, in spite of their not being subject any longer to the governance of the soul.

ROBERT KOCH, winner of the 1905 Nobel prize in physiology and medicine for his work on tuberculosis, was one of the founders of the science of bacteriology.

Early work on bacterial disease was hampered by the inability to cultivate disease-producing bacteria outside the body, and to isolate one species of bacteria from another. In the following article, Koch describes how he used a boiled potato cut in half as a solid medium for developing pure bacterial cultures. This great achievement marked the beginning of a rational system of bacterial culturing.

Koch's postulates are still studied by every student of bacteriology. They state that (1) a specific organism must be seen in all cases of an infectious disease; (2) this organism must be obtained in pure culture; (3) organisms from pure cultures must reproduce the disease in experimental animals; (4) the organism must be recoverable from the experimental animals. Although there are some diseases to which these postulates do not apply—leprosy being a notable example—they have been invaluable guides to the discovery of the etiologic agents in many of the most common diseases of men, animals and plants.

On the Investigation of Pathogenic Organisms

From Robert Koch, "On the Investigation of Pathogenic Organisms." Reprinted by permission from *Moments of Discovery*, edited by George Schwartz and Philip W. Bishop, © 1958 by Basic Books, Inc., Publishers, New York.

As A RULE the following points must be observed in investigating microorganisms from the point of view of sanitary science. In the first place, it must be definitely determined whether the organisms are pathogenic at all, that is to say, whether they can cause disease. Following on that comes the proof of their inoculability, that is, of the possibility of their being transferred from one individual to another previously healthy; this transfer being attempted both on individuals belonging to the same species as those in whom the disease arose spontaneously or was artificially produced and on individuals of other species.

Next we have to trace out the mode in which the pathogenic organisms enter the animal body, to follow their behaviour outside the body in the air, water, and soil and finally to determine what influence reagents exert on them in the way of destroying them or preventing their development. . . .

Bacteria have one peculiarity which makes it possible to overcome the difficulties presented by their extremely small size. This peculiarity is simply the power of taking up and retaining the colours of certain dyes, especially the anilines. . . . The process of making the bacteria in fluids such as blood, pus, and lymph visible by means of stains, consists in spreading the fluid containing them in as thin a layer as possible on a cover glass, drying it, and then subjecting it to the action of the staining solution. . . .

By the methods described above the existence of microorganisms in animal tissues may be demonstrated, and if the investigation shows that they are present in large numbers, or that they have caused irritation or gangrene in the invaded tissues, their pathogenic power is thus made certain. A second question which interests us is whether these microorganisms, which are known to be pathogenic, are also infectious, that is whether they can be transferred from one animal to another. The terms infectious and pathogenic must not be confused with one another; it is perfectly possible to conceive the existence of organisms which, since they can penetrate in the tissues of the animal body and set up diseases therein, are truly pathogenic, but still have not the power of infecting, that is, of passing from one animal to another and causing disease in that one also. . . . The terms pathogenic and infectious are not, therefore, identical, and if a parasite is shown to be pathogenic it must be experimentally established in addition whether it is infectious or not.

In order that our procedures should be rewarded by a positive result, the conditions existing in nature must be adhered to as closely as possible, a precaution which was neglected in the early days of experimental research into infectious diseases. People have experimentally endeavoured in the most primitive way to communicate to dogs, cats, rabbits, guinea pigs, and the like, diseases which have hitherto only been observed in man. Experience has, however, taught us that it is not a matter of indifference what species of animal is employed for the experiment, and that the method by which the inoculation is performed has the greatest influence on the success of the experiment. . . .

All instruments employed in infection experiments must, of couse, be subjected to trustworthy disinfection which according to my experience in this sort of work is only to be obtained by prolonged heating at 150° C. and above. One often reads that disinfection was accomplished by the aid of alcohol, carbolic acid, and the like, but the experiments on the action of various disinfectants on the spores of *Bacillus anthracis* which are described elsewhere show how untrustworthy these substances are. . , .

There is still one indispensable condition attached to all experiments on infection, viz., that no reliance should be placed on one experiment, and that the requisite control experiments should never be omitted. How often one meets with the statement that some suspected substance or fluid had been inoculated into an animal, or injected subcutaneously; that the animal fell ill, and possibly died, and that this fatal result was clearly a direct result of the inoculation, and that the illness was an example of the affection in question. And yet it is quite evident that a single such experiment is as good as useless. For in the first place, it must be shown that this solitary result was neither a mistake nor an accident, and that the inoculation can produce in the animals experimented upon in every case, or in a very large majority of cases, the disease or death, so that every accidental circumstance may be excluded. A further point, and one on which I lay special stress, seeing how often it is omitted, is the necessity of first making certain that one has to do with a really infective material. The fact that a material when injected subcutaneously, or into a vein, or into the abdominal cavity or elsewhere, causes a pathogenic effect, does not in the least show that this material possesses infective power. . . . Only when it can be shown that a disease is successfully communicated from one individual to another by such a small quantity of the infective material that to have produced the disease it must have multiplied in the body, can such a material be regarded as infective. From this it follows that if anyone wishes to know for certain whether he is experimenting with an infective material he cannot possibly remain satisfied with one experiment, but must carry out a more or less extensive and continuous series of inoculations from one animal to a second, from that to a third and so on, before he can get rid of the just objection that he is only dealing with the symptoms of simple poisoning and not with those of an infective disease.

Pure Cultivations

After the presence of pathogenic organisms in the body has been definitely ascertained, as well as their capability of multiplying in the tissues, and their communicability from one individual to another, there yet remains a most interesting and most important hygienic problem, namely, the demonstration of the conditions of their growth. It has already been shown at the beginning of this paper that this problem is only to be solved by the aid of pure cultivations of the microorganisms, and it is no exaggeration to say that pure cultivations are the crux of all researches into infective diseases. . . . The essential principles of pure cultivation as it is practised may now be condensed as follows.

A sterile nutrient fluid is placed in a disinfected glass vessel, which is plugged "fungus-tight" with disinfected cotton wool, and then this fluid is inoculated with the material containing the microorganisms of which a pure culture is to be obtained. If growth occurs in these first flasks, then fur-

ther inoculation is performed from these into a second series of similarly prepared vessels by means of a disinfected instrument. In fact it is almost exactly the same process as in transmitting an infective disease from one animal to another.

Obviously, various precautions are employed in these methods, the first of which is to see that the cultivation vessel is really disinfected. . . . The second precaution must be to see that the wool plug really fits so closely as to exclude all fungi. . . . Thirdly, the nutrient fluid must be of suitable composition, and thoroughly sterilized. . . . Fourthly, the substance to be inoculated must contain only the microorganism of which a pure cultivation is required and no other, for if there is the slightest contamination of the infective material with a more rapidly growing form of microorganism than that which one desires to cultivate, one cannot, as Buchner has very strikingly shown, possibly succeed in getting the desired pure cultivation. . . . Fifthly, precautions must be taken that no spores of extraneous organisms from the air fall into the culture fluid while the first inoculation, and indeed while every subsequent inoculation, is being made. This is a risk which no experimenter can ever protect his pure cultures from with absolute certainty. Even if he takes out the protecting wool plug only for an extremely short time, even though the early cultivations are successful, the probability increases with each further inoculation that a contamination will occur.

I have abandoned the principles on which pure cultures have hitherto been conducted, and have struck out on a new path, to which I was led by a simple observation, which anyone can repeat. If a boiled potato is divided and then the cut surface exposed to the air for a few hours, and then placed in a moist chamber (as, for instance, on a plate under a bell jar lined with wet filter paper) so as to prevent drying, there will be found by the second or third day (according to the temperature of the room) on the surface of the potato numerous and very varied droplets, almost all of which appear to differ from each other. A few of these droplets are white and porcellanous, while others are yellow, brown, grey, or reddish; and while some appear like a flattened out drop of water, others are hemispherical or warty. All grow more or less rapidly, and between them appears the mycelium of the higher fungi; later the solitary droplets become fused together and soon marked decomposition of the potato occurs. If a specimen is taken from each of these droplets so long as they remain distinctly isolated from each other, and is examined by drying and staining a layer of it on a cover glass, it will be seen that each is composed of a perfectly definite kind of microorganism. One, for example, will show enormous micrococci, another very minute ones, a third may show micrococci arranged in chains while other colonies, especially those which spread out flat like a membrane, are composed of bacilli of various size and arrangement. . . . The source of all these different organisms will not long remain a matter of doubt if another potato is taken, and peeled with a previously heated knife, so that none of the skin may remain which might contain, at least in the earth clinging to it, spores of bacilli which had not been killed by the brief boiling. It must not be exposed to the air, but kept in a disinfected vessel which is plugged with wool, under which circumstances it will be found that no droplets appear, no orga-

nisms settle on it, and consequently it remains unaltered, until after several weeks it becomes dried up. That the organisms which developed as small droplike colonies on the first potato fell on it from the air is obvious, and indeed one often finds a small particle of dust or thread in the centre of the small colony which has clearly served as a carrier of the organisms, whether as dry but still living bacteria, as spores, or as yeast cells. . . .

The question now arises, what do we learn from this observation of these colonies growing on potatoes? We learn this most striking fact, that with a few exceptions, every droplet or colony is a pure culture, and remains so until by growth it pushes into the territory of a neighbour, and the individuals of each colony mingle. . . . If an equally broad surface of a nutrient fluid, instead of the potato had been exposed to the influence of the air, numerous organisms would without doubt have fallen into it, indeed approximately as many kinds as in the case of the potato, but their development would have proceeded very differently. The motile bacteria would have dispersed themselves rapidly throughout the fluid, and would have become mixed with the immobile ones, which at first develop to some extent in small floating colonies. . . . To sum up: the whole fluid would from the beginning afford on microscopical examination a picture of a confused mixture of different forms and never even in the remotest sense of the word could be called a pure cultivation. In what lies the marked difference between the soil which is offered by the potato and by the fluid respectively? It only consists in this, that the former is a solid soil and prevents the different kinds of organisms (even those which are motile) from mixing with one another, whilst with regard to the latter, the fluid substratum, there is no possibility of the different species remaining separate from one another.

It becomes important to utilize further the advantages which a solid cultivation soil offers for pure cultivations. . . . I devoted my attention to discover how well-known and new nutrient solutions could be converted from the fluid into the solid condition; and I found the best way of accomplishing this was to mix gelatine with the nutrient liquid. . . .

The mixture of nutrient fluid and gelatine which I shall call "nutrient jelly" is prepared in the following way: gelatine is soaked in distilled water and then dissolved by heat. To it is added the nutrient fluid in such quantity that the mixture shall contain in definite proportions the necessary quantities of gelatine and nutritive material. I

have found the most convenient amount of gelatine in the nutrient-gelatine mixture to be about 2½ to 3 per cent. . . .

The peculiarity of my method is that it supplies a firm, and where possible a transparent pabulum; that its composition can be varied to any extent, and suited to the organism under observation; that all precautions against the possibility of after-contamination are rendered superfluous; that subsequent cultivation can be carried out by a larger number of single cultures, of which, of course, only those cultures which remain pure are employed for further cultivation; and that finally, a constant control over the state of the culture can be obtained by the use of the microscope. In almost all these points my method differs from those hitherto employed, and especially also from the former attempts at cultivation with potatoes and isinglass referred to above.

JULY 6, 1885, Joseph Meister, age nine, bitten and mauled by a mad dog, is brought to the laboratory of Louis Pasteur, the most famous microbiologist of his time and developer of vaccines against disease. At eight o'clock that night, young Joseph becomes a unique figure on the stage of medical history—the first person to be innoculated against rabies. Nowhere would Pasteur's remark that "chance favors the prepared mind" be more dramatically applied than to his unexpected treatment of Joseph Meister, which Pasteur describes so vividly in the following article.

Before his development of rabies vaccine, Pasteur had isolated the germ of chicken cholera. By cultivating an attenuated form of the germ and inoculating fowls with the culture, he rendered them immune from virulent attacks of cholera.

Pasteur then turned his attention to anthrax, a disease of cattle and sheep. Following the same methods that he had used in cholera research, he isolated the bacillus, and by cultivating it in oxygen at a temperature of 42°C, produced attenuated germs that made the inoculated animal immune against a culture of full strength. Pasteur called his method vaccination.

The vaccine that was to save Joseph Meister's life had been painstakingly prepared and passed through different species of animals by Pasteur until its virulence had abated. Interestingly, Pasteur was never able to observe the actual rabies germ. He assumed it must be too small to be seen under a microscope. The virus theory of disease was not then in existence.

An ironic footnote in the life of Joseph Meister is the manner of his death 55 years after his treatment by Pasteur. Meister became the gatekeeper of the Pasteur Institute, established in 1888 to treat cases of rabies. It is now a center for biological research. In 1940, the Nazis ordered Meister to open Pasteur's crypt in the Institute. Rather than obey the Nazis, Meister killed himself.

On Preventing Rabies

From Louis Pasteur in *Recent Essays on Bacteria in Relation to Disease*, edited by W. W. Cheyne (1886). Reprinted by permission from *Moments of Discovery*, edited by George Schwartz and Philip W. Bishop, © 1958 by Basic Books, Inc., Publishers, New York.

A Method by which the Development of Rabies after a Bite May Be Prevented

A real progress in the study of rabies was marked, without any doubt, by the papers in which I announced, in my own name and in the name of my fellow-workers, a prophylactic method; but the progress was scientific rather than practical. Accidents were liable to occur in its application. Of twenty dogs treated, I could not undertake to render more than fifteen or sixteen refractory to rabies.

Further, it was desirable, at the end of the treatment, to inoculate with a very virulent virus—a control virus—in order to confirm and reinforce the refractory condition. More than this, prudence demanded that the dogs should be kept under observation during a period longer than the period of incubation of the disease produced by the direct inoculation of this last virus. Therefore, in order to be quite sure that the refractory state had been produced, it was sometimes necessary to wait three or four months. The application of the method would have been very much limited by these troublesome conditions.

Finally, the method did not lend itself easily to the immediate treatment rendered necessary by the accidental and unforeseen way in which bites are inflicted by rabid animals.

It was necessary, therefore, to discover, if possible, a more rapid method, and yet one, I would venture to say, capable of affording perfect security to dogs. Otherwise who would have the temerity, before this progress had been achieved, to make any experiment on man?

After making almost innumerable experiments, I have discovered a prophylactic method which is practical and prompt, and which has already in dogs afforded me results sufficiently numerous, certain, and successful, to warrant my having confidence in its general applicability to all animals, and even to man himself.

This method depends essentially on the following facts:

The inoculation under the *dura mater*, after trephining, of the infective spinal cord of a dog suffering from ordinary rabies (*rage des rues*), always produces rabies in rabbits after a period of incubation having a mean duration of about fifteen days.

If, by the above method of inoculation, the virus of the first rabbit is passed into a second, and that of the second into a third, and so on, in series, a more and more striking tendency is soon manifested towards a diminution of the duration of the incubation period of rabies in the rabbits successively inoculated.

After passing twenty or twenty-five times from rabbit to rabbit, inoculation periods of eight days are met with, and continue for another interval, during which the virus is passed twenty or twenty-five times from rabbit to rabbit. Then an incubation period of seven days is reached, which is encountered with striking regularity throughout a new series extending as far as the ninetieth animal. This at least is the number which I have reached at the present time, and the most that can be said is that a slight tendency is manifested towards an incubation period of a little less than seven days.

Experiments of this class, begun in No-

vember 1882, have now lasted for three years without any break in the continuity of the series, and without our ever being obliged to have recourse to any other virus than that of the rabbits successively dead of rabies. Consequently, nothing is easier than to have constantly at our disposal, over considerable intervals of time, a virus of rabies, quite pure, and always quite or very nearly identical. This is the central fact in the practical application of the method.

The virus of rabies at a constant degree of virulence is contained in the spinal cords of these rabbits throughout their whole extent.

If portions, a few centimetres long, are removed from these spinal cords with every possible precaution to preserve their purity, and are then suspended in dry air, the virulence slowly disappears, until at last it entirely vanishes. The time within which this extinction of virulence is brought about varies a little with the thickness of the morsels of spinal cord, but chiefly with the external temperature. The lower the temperature the longer is the virulence preserved. These results form the central scientific point in the method.

These facts being established, a dog may be rendered refractory to rabies in a relatively short time in the following way:

Every day morsels of fresh infective spinal cord from a rabbit which has died of rabies developed after an incubation period of seven days, are suspended in a series of flasks, the air in which is kept dry by placing fragments of potash at the bottom of the flask. Every day also a dog is inoculated under the skin with a Pravaz' syringe full of sterilized broth, in which a small fragment of one of the spinal cords has been broken up, commencing with a spinal cord far enough removed in order of time from the day of the operation to render it certain that the cord was not at all virulent. (This date had been ascertained by previous experiments.) On the following days the same operation is performed with more recent cords, separated from each other by an interval of two days, until at last a very virulent cord, which has only been in the flask for two days, is used.

The dog has now been rendered refractory to rabies. It may be inoculated with the virus of rabies under the skin, or even after trephining, on the surface of the brain, without any subsequent development of rabies.

Never having once failed when using this method, I had in my possession fifty dogs, of all ages and of every race, refractory to rabies, when three individuals from Alsace unexpectedly presented themselves at my laboratory, on Monday the 6th of last July.

Théodore Vone, grocer, of Meissengott, near Schlestadt, bitten in the arm, July 4th, by his own dog, which had gone mad.

Joseph Meister, aged nine years, also bitten on July 4th, at eight o'clock in the morning, by the same dog. This child had been knocked over by the dog and presented numerous bites, on the hands, legs, and thighs, some of them so deep as to render walking difficult. The principal bites had been cauterized at eight o'clock in the evening of July 4th, only twelve hours after the accident, with phenic acid, by Dr Weber, of Villé.

The third person, who had not been bitten, was the mother of little Joseph Meister.

At the examination of the dog, after its death by the hand of its master, the stomach was found full of hay, straw, and scraps of wood. The dog was certainly rabid. Joseph Meister had been pulled out from under him covered with foam and blood.

M. Vone had some severe contusions on the arm, but he assured me that his shirt had not been pierced by the dog's fangs. As he had nothing to fear, I told him that he could return to Alsace the same day, which he did, but I kept young Meister and his mother with me.

The weekly meeting of the Académie des Sciences took place on July 6th. At it I met our colleague Dr Vulpian, to whom I related what had just happened. M. Vulpian, and Dr Grancher, Professor in the Faculté de Médecine, had the goodness to come and see little Joseph Meister at once, and to take note of the condition and the number of his wounds. There were no less than fourteen.

The opinion of our learned colleague, and of Dr Grancher, was that, owing to the severity and the number of the bites, Joseph Meister was almost certain to take rabies. I then communicated to M. Vulpian and to M. Grancher the new results which I had obtained from the study of rabies since the address which I had given at Copenhagen a year earlier.

The death of this child appearing to be inevitable, I decided, not without lively and sore anxiety, as may well be believed, to try upon Joseph Meister the method which I had found constantly successful with dogs.

My fifty dogs, it is true, had not been bitten before I brought them into the condition of being refractory to rabies; but I knew that that circumstance might be left out of my calculations, because I had previously rendered a large number of dogs refractory to rabies after they had been bitten. I have this year given the members of the Commission de la Rage evidence of this new and important advance.

Consequently, on July 6th, at 8 o'clock in the evening, sixty hours after the bites on July 4th, and in the presence of Drs Vulpian and Grancher, young Meister was inoculated under a fold of skin raised in the right hypochondrium, with half a Pravaz' syringeful of the spinal cord of a rabbit, which had died of rabies on June 21st. It had been preserved since then, that is to say, fifteen days, in a flask of dry air.

On the following days fresh inoculations were made. I thus made thirteen inoculations, and prolonged the treatment to ten days. I shall say later on that a smaller number of inoculations would have been sufficient. But it will be understood how, in the first attempt, I would act with a very special circumspection.

The days following, new inoculations were made, always in the hypochondrial region according to the conditions which I give in the following table:

July	Time	Cord taken	Dried for
7	9 a.m.	June 23	14 days
7	6 p.m.	June 25	12 days
8	9 a.m.	June 27	11 days
8	6 p.m.	June 29	9 days
9	11 a.m.	July 1	8 days
10	11 a.m.	July 3	7 days
11	11 a.m.	July 5	6 days
12	11 a.m.	July 7	5 days
13	11 a.m.	July 9	4 days
14	11 a.m.	July 11	3 days
15	11 a.m.	July 13	2 days
16	11 a.m.	July 15	1 day

In order to follow the condition as to virulence of the spinal cords, two fresh rabbits were inoculated, by trephining, with the various spinal cords employed.

Observation of these rabbits enabled us to ascertain that the spinal cords of July 6th, 7th, 8th, 9th, 10th, were not virulent, for they did not render the rabbits rabid; the spinal cords of July 11th, 12th, 14th, 15th, 16th, were all virulent, and the virulent material was present in larger and larger proportion. Rabies appeared after an incubation of seven days in the rabbits of July 15th and 16th; after eight days in those of the 12th and 14th; after fifteen days in those of July 11th.

On the last days, therefore, I had inoculated Joseph Meister with the most virulent virus of rabies, that, namely of the dog, reinforced by passing a great number of times from rabbit to rabbit, a virus which produced rabies after seven days' incubation in these animals, after eight or ten days in dogs.

When the condition of immunity has been attained, the most virulent virus can be inoculated, in considerable quantity, without ill effects. It has always seemed to me that the only possible effect of this must be to make immunity more assured.

Joseph Meister, therefore, has escaped, not only the rabies which would have been caused by the bites he received, but also the rabies with which I have inoculated him in order to test the immunity produced by the treatment, a rabies more virulent than ordinary canine rabies.

The final inoculation with very virulent virus has this further advantage, that it puts a period to the apprehensions which arise as to the consequences of the bites. If rabies could occur it would declare itself more quickly after a more virulent virus than after the virus of the bites. Since the middle of August I have looked forward with confidence to the future good health of Joseph Meister. At the present time, three months and three weeks having elapsed since the accident, his state of health leaves nothing to be desired.

What interpretation is to be given to this new method which I have just made known, of preventing rabies after bites? I have not at the present moment any intention of treating this question in a complete manner. I wish to confine myself to certain preliminary details essential to the comprehension of the significance of the experiments, which I am continuing, in order to adopt eventually the best of the various possible interpretations.

Bearing in mind the methods of progressively attenuating various lethal virus, and the prophylaxis in that way attained, and admitting also the influence of the air in bringing about this attenuation the first explanation to account for the effects of this method which suggests itself is, that while the morsels of spinal cord are left in contact with the dry air, the intensity of their virulence is progressively diminished, until it is entirely abolished.

This reflection would lead us to believe that the prophylactic method now described depended upon the employment at first of a virus without any appreciable ac-

tivity, then of feeble intensity, and then of more and more virulence.

I will show that facts do not lend support to this view. I will prove that the increase in the length of the period of incubation of the rabies, each day, communicated to the rabbits, as I have just described, in order to test the virulence of the spinal-cords dried on contact with air, is an effect of a diminution of the quantity of the virus of rabies contained in the spinal cords, and not an effect of a diminution of its virulence. . . .

In conclusion I need not say that perhaps the most important of the problems to be solved at the present time is that of the interval which may be allowed between the occurrence of the bites and the commencement of the treatment. In the case of Joseph Meister this interval was two days and a half. But it must be expected to be often much longer.

On Tuesday last, October 20th, with the kind assistance of MM. Vulpian and Grancher, I commenced to treat a youth of fifteen years, bitten six full days before, on both hands, under exceptionally grave circumstances. I will promptly make known to the academy the result of this new trial.

IN PRECEDING ARTICLES, both Kircher and Pasteur postulated the existence of disease-producing agents too small to be seen. In 1890, Dimitri Iwanowsky, a Russian bacteriologist, observed that the agent responsible for the tobacco mosaic disease would pass through the pores of a bacteria-trapping filter. He reported his observation, though he eventually concluded that there was a flaw in the filter and that the disease-producing agent was bacterial.

In 1898, M. W. Beijerinck, a Dutch botanist also working on the tobacco mosaic disease, announced that the infectious agent of the disease was not bacterial, but what he called a filterable virus (*virus* being the Latin word for "poison").

In the following article, Iwanowsky describes his experiment on the mosaic disease of the tobacco plant. His observations contributed to the gathering evidence for a class of disease agents that not only produces an ailment of the tobacco plant, but is also responsible for polio, mumps, chicken pox, flu and the common cold—the viruses.

On the Mosaic Disease of the Tobacco Plant

From Dm. Iwanowsky, *Bulletine de l'Académie Impériale des Sciences*, Vol. 35, p. 67 (1892), translated by M. L. Gabriel in *Great Experiments in Biology*, edited by Mordecai L. Gabriel and Seymour Fogel, © 1955. Reprinted by permission of Prentice-Hall, Inc., Englewood Cliffs, N. J.

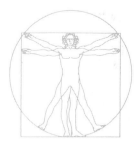

TWO YEARS AGO I described, jointly with Mr. W. Polowzow, a very widespread disease of tobacco which we named pox disease and the cause of which we then set forth. On that occasion we expressed the view that the mosaic disease of tobacco described by Ad. Mayer in Holland is actually separable into two distinct diseases, of which one (according to Mayer, the second phase of the mosaic disease) is the pox disease studied by us. During an investigation of the diseases of tobacco in Crimea in the summer of 1890 I was able to convince myself of the complete correctness of the opinion expressed by us at that time, since I also encountered there the disease form which Mayer had described as the first phase of the mosaic disease and I was able to ascertain that this form is an entirely independent, and in many respects a very interesting disease. (I shall designate it as mosaic disease, although it represents only one developmental stage of the disease described by Mayer under this name.) Among the tobacco growers of that region (Tatars) it is known merely by the name "Bosuch" (i.e., sickness); by some it is also called marble-disease. The outward appearance of the diseased plant, the developmental course of the disease, and its distribution on the plantation fully agree with the descriptions of Mayer, so that it is not necessary for me to discuss this question further. The difference in appearance first begins at the point where Mayer asserts that "if the disease develops further in typical fashion, some of the lighter and thinner parts of the leaf die prematurely, not unlike but much more extensively than a similar dotted necrosis which often occurs in fully ripe leaves, without detriment to the quality of the product." In the accompanying plate [not included], Mayer depicts a leaf thickly covered with brown spots; these spots are here and there run together and some of them have fallen out of the leaf, so that as a consequence the leaf appears to have broad openings. In my opinion, the pictured leaf has been attacked by two quite different diseases: the mosaic disease (in the sense adopted by me) and the pox disease. Both diseases, although they are of quite different origins can naturally occur on one and the same plant. (It is even possible that plants attacked by the mosaic disease succumb more easily to the pox disease than healthy plants because sick plants fall prey more readily than healthy plants especially to new diseases.) The brown spots are, however, for the most part not connected with the yellow parts of leaves attacked by mosaic disease as should be the case according to Mayer's view; not infrequently one can find them in the middle of the dark green healthy part. On the contrary, the independence of the two diseases cannot any longer be subject to doubt. In support of this may I adduce the following facts:

(1.) Neither in Little Russia nor in Bessarabia have I encountered the mosaic disease, although the pox disease is very prevalent there.

(2.) In Crimea, where both diseases occur, one can find, on inspection of the tobacco plants, examples affected only by mosaic disease, and others only by pox disease. These plants can most readily be distinguished according to the very young leaves. In plants attacked by the mosaic disease (as Mayer also has observed) all further new growths (new leaflets and shoots) display the characteristic changes of this disease, namely mosaic patterns consisting of dark green and yellow patches. Hence, when we encounter examples of brown-spotted tobacco plants in which the young leaves show no trace of mosaic pattern, we can say definitely that these plants are suffering from pox disease.

(3.) The mosaic disease is contagious while the pox disease, on the contrary, does not possess this property.

(4.) The cause of the pox disease lies in the conditions of transpiration of water from the leaves; the spots appear in completely healthy leaves upon occurrence of a quick and sudden increase in the plant's transpiration. The causes of the mosaic disease are, on the contrary, quite different; it is, as previously mentioned, infectious.

(5.) The pox disease is found in *Datura Stramonium, Hyoscyamus niger* and many other plants; the mosaic disease, on the other hand, according to Mayer's experience, is not transmitted to other representatives of the family Solanaceae.

In favor of the view that both diseases represent different developmental stages of one and the same disease, Mayer cites only the similar range of distribution and their succession in time: "To be sure, some workers," writes Mayer, "wish to recognize in both forms, or better, stages, of the disease, two independent diseases, but only for the reason that the first stage frequently escapes superficial observation. The similar range of distribution and the succession in time of the two forms argue completely against this."

My investigations on the mosaic disease are not yet completed, since I have encountered great difficulties which must first be overcome (as, for example, the inability of the tobacco mosaic microbes to develop on the usual artificial media). Yet I am already in a position to confirm the following statements of Mayer:

(1.) *that the juice of plants affected with tobacco mosaic disease is infectious;* when introduced into healthy plants after a certain time it evokes in them the tobacco mosaic disease;

(2.) *that upon being heated to a temperature near the boiling point, the juice loses its infectious properties;*

(3.) *that the infectiousness of the disease, in consideration of the absence of fungi and other parasites, must be attributed to Bacteria.*

On the other hand, I must most definitely contradict the assertion of this author that the juice of leaves affected by mosaic loses its infective characteristics after filtration through a double layer of filter paper. In my experience the filtered extract of diseased leaves when transferred to healthy leaves produces the disease symptoms as effectively as the unfiltered juice. On the other hand, this statement of the author does not accord with the view that the mosaic disease is caused by bacteria, since a double layer of filter paper, as is known, cannot hold back bacteria. If this observation of Mayer were correct, one would then have to reach the conclusion that the mosaic disease is caused, not by bacteria, but by fungi, the spores of which cannot pass through filter paper. I have, however, found *that the juice of leaves affected by mosaic disease retains its contagious properties even after filtration through Chamberland filter candles.* According to the currently prevailing views, the latter observation is most simply explained, it seems to me, by the assumption of a toxin, secreted by the bacteria present in the tobacco plants, which is dissolved in the filtered juice. Besides this, however, another likewise tenable explanation is possible: namely that the bacteria in the tobacco plant penetrate through the pores of the Chamberland filter candle, although before every experiment I tested the filter which I was using in the usual manner and I made certain of the absence of fine cracks and openings. (Through a filter candle immersed in a cylinder of water no air could be forced by means of a rubber bulb.) As a further positive proof of the effectiveness of the filter candle I used, I regard the fact that liquids most favorable for the development of bacteria remained completely unchanged for several months after filtration through these candles. In any case, further investigation will, I hope, clarify this question; the foregoing short note has only the purpose of establishing the independence of the two diseases—the mosaic and the pox disease—and showing that they do not represent, as Ad. Mayer believes, different stages of development of the same disease.

VI

ALEXANDER FLEMING, a British bacteriologist particularly interested in bacterial action and antiseptics, describes in the following article his epochal discovery in 1928 of the antibacterial powers of the mold from which penicillin is derived.

Labeled "a triumph of accident and shrewd observation," Fleming's discovery occurred while he was working with cultures of staphylococcus for research he was doing on influenza. He noted that mold had grown on some old culture plates he intended to throw away and that the mold had created a bacteria-free circle around itself. Fleming cultured the mold and attempted to identify its active agent. He could not, but found that it was closely related to the common variety of mold often found growing on bread. Since the generic name of this type of mold is *Penicillium*, he named the filtrate from it penicillin. Experimenting further, he found that the substance prevented growth of staphylococci, even when diluted 800 times.

In spite of the great significance of Fleming's discovery, published in *The British Journal of Experimental Pathology* in 1929, no immediate interest was shown in it. It was not until World War II produced an urgent need for new antibacterials for the treatment of wounds that penicillin was given serious consideration. This need, coupled with advances in chemistry, enabled Sir Howard Walter Florey and Ernst Boris Chain to isolate, identify and purify the active agent involved. The world now had its first antibiotic.

In 1945, Fleming, along with Florey and Chain, received the Nobel prize in medicine and physiology for their work on penicillin.

On The Antibacterial Action of Cultures of Penicillium

From Alexander Fleming, "On the Antibacterial Action of Cultures of Penicillium, with Special Reference to Their Use in the Isolation of *B. influenzæ*," *The British Journal of Experimental Pathology*, Vol. 10, No. 3 (1929), pp. 226-236. Reprinted by permission of the publisher and Mrs. Amalia Fleming.

WHILE working with staphylococcus variants a number of culture plates were set aside on the laboratory bench and examined from time to time. In the examinations these plates were necessarily exposed to the air and they became contaminated with various micro-organisms. It was noticed that around a large colony of a contaminating mould the staphylococcus colonies became transparent and were obviously undergoing lysis.

Subcultures of this mould were made and experiments conducted with a view to ascertaining something of the properties of the bacteriolytic substance which had evidently been formed in the mould culture and which had diffused into the surrounding medium. It was found that broth in which the mould had been grown at room temperature for one or two weeks had acquired marked inhibitory, bactericidal and bacteriolytic properties to many of the more common pathogenic bacteria.

Characters of the Mould

The colony appears as a white fluffy mass which rapidly increases in size and after a few days sporulates, the centre becoming dark green and later in old cultures darkens to almost black. In four or five days a bright yellow colour is produced which diffuses into the medium. In certain conditions a reddish colour can be observed in the growth.

In broth the mould grows on the surface as a white fluffy growth changing in a few days to a dark green felted mass. The broth becomes bright yellow and this yellow pigment is not extracted by CHCl₃. The reaction of the broth becomes markedly alkaline, the pH varying from 8.5 to 9. Acid is produced in three or four days in glucose and saccharose broth. There is no acid production in 7 days in lactose, mannite or dulcite broth.

Growth is slow at 37°C. and is most rapid about 20°C. No growth is observed under anaerobic conditions.

In its morphology this organism is a penicillium and in all its characters it most closely resembles *P. rubrum*. Biourge (1923) states that he has never found *P. rubrum* in nature and that it is an "animal de laboratoire." This penicillium is not uncommon in the air of the laboratory.

Is the Antibacterial Body Elaborated in Culture by All Moulds?

A number of other moulds were grown in broth at room temperature and the culture fluids were tested for antibacterial substances at various intervals up to one month. The species examined were: *Eidamia viridiscens, Botrytis cineria, Aspergillus fumigatus, Sporotrichum, Cladosporium, Penicillium*, 8 strains. Of these it was found that only one strain of penicillium produced any inhibitory substance, and that one had exactly the same cultural characters as the original one from the contaminated plate.

It is clear, therefore, that the production of this antibacterial substance is not common to all moulds or to all types of penicillium.

In the rest of this article allusion will constantly be made to experiments with filtrates of a broth culture of this mould, so for convenience and to avoid the repetition of the rather cumbersome phrase "Mould broth filtrate," the name "penicillin" will be used. This will denote the filtrate of a broth culture of the particular penicillium with which we are concerned.

Methods of Examining Cultures for Antibacterial Substance

The simplest method of examining for inhibitory power is to cut a furrow in an agar plate (or a plate of other suitable culture material), and fill this in with a mixture of equal parts of agar and the broth in which the mould has grown. When this has solidified, cultures of various microbes can be streaked at right angles from the furrow to the edge of the plate. The inhibitory substance diffuses very rapidly in the agar, so that in the few hours before the microbes show visible growth it has spread out for a centimetre or more in sufficient concentration to inhibit growth of a sensitive microbe. On further incubation it will be seen that the proximal portion of the culture for perhaps one centimetre becomes transparent, and on examination of this portion of the culture it is found that practically all the microbes are dissolved, indicating that the anti-bacterial substance has continued to diffuse into the agar in sufficient concentration to induce dissolution of the bacteria. This simple method therefore suffices to demonstrate the bacterio-inhibitory and bacteriolytic properties of the mould culture, and also by the extent of the area of inhibition gives some measure of the sensitiveness of the particular microbe tested. Figure 1 shows the degree of inhibition obtained with various microbes tested in this way. (NOTE: Figure 1 not shown.)

The inhibitory power can be accurately titrated by making serial dilutions of penicillin in fresh nutrient broth, and then implanting all the tubes with the same volume of a bacterial suspension and incubating them. The inhibition can then readily be seen by noting the opacity of the broth.

For the estimation of the antibacterial power of a mould culture it is unnecessary to filter as the mould grows only slowly at 37° C., and in 24 hours, when the results are read, no growth of mould is perceptible. Staphylococcus is a very suitable microbe on which to test the broth as it is hardy, lives well in culture, grows rapidly, and is very sensitive to penicillin.

The bactericidal power can be tested in the same way except that at intervals measured quantities are explanted so that the number of surviving microbes can be estimated.

Properties of the Antibacterial Substance

EFFECT OF HEAT

Heating for 1 hour at 56° or 80° C. has no effect on the antibacterial power of penicillin. Boiling for a few minutes hardly affects it (see table 2). Boiling for 1 hour reduces it to less than one quarter its previous strength if the fluid is alkaline, but if it is neutral or very slightly acid then the reduction is much less. Autoclaving for 20 minutes at 115° C. practically destroys it.

EFFECT OF FILTRATION

Passage through a Seitz filter does not diminish the antibacterial power. This is the best method of obtaining sterile active mould broth.

SOLUBILITY

It is freely soluble in water and weak saline solutions. My colleague, Mr. Ridley, has found that if penicillin is evaporated at a low temperature to a sticky mass the active principle can be completely extracted by absolute alcohol. It is insoluble in ether or chloroform.

RATE OF DEVELOPMENT OF INHIBITORY SUBSTANCE IN CULTURE

A 500 c.c. Erlenmeyer flask containing 200 c.c. of broth was planted with mould spores and incubated at room temperature (10° to 20° C.). The inhibitory power of the broth to staphylococcus was tested at intervals.

After 5 days complete inhibition in 1 in 20   dilution
After 6 days complete inhibition in 1 in 40   dilution
After 7 days complete inhibition in 1 in 200 dilution
After 8 days complete inhibition in 1 in 500 dilution

Grown at 20° C. the development of the active principle is more rapid and a good sample will completely inhibit staphylococci in a 1 in 500 or 1 in 800 dilution in 6 or 7 days. As the culture ages the antibacterial power falls and may in 14 days at 20° C. have almost disappeared.

The antibacterial power of penicillin falls when it is kept at room temperature. The rate of this fall can be seen from table 1.

If the reaction of penicillin is altered from its original pH of 9 to pH of 6.8 it is much more stable.

The small drops of bright yellow fluid which collect on the surface of the mould may have a high antibacterial titre. One specimen of such fluid completely inhibited the growth of staphylococci in a dilution of 1 in 20,000 while the broth in which the mould was growing, tested at the same time, inhibited staphylococcal growth in 1 in 800.

If the mould is grown on solid medium and the felted mass picked off and extracted in normal salt solution for 24 hours it is found that the extract has bacteriolytic properties.

TABLE 1.

Effect of Keeping at Room Temperature on the Anti-Staphylococcal Power of Penicillin

Growth of staphylococcus in dilutions of penicillin as under.

	1/20.	1/40.	1/60.	1/80.	1/100.	1/200.	1/300.	1/400.	1/600.	1/800.	1/1000.	Control.
At time of filtration	−	−	−	−	−	−	−	−	−	±	+ +	+ +
After 4 days	−	−	−	−	−	−	−	−	−	±	+ +	+ +
After 7 days	−	−	−	−	−	−	−	±	+	+	+ +	+ +
After 9 days	−	−	−	−	−	−	−	±	+	+	+ +	+ +
After 13 days	−	−	−	−	−	+	+	+	+	+	+ +	+ +
After 15 days	−	±	+	+	+	+	+	+	+	+	+ +	+ +

If this extract is mixed with a thick suspension of staphylococcus suspension and incubated for 2 hours at 45° C. it will be found that the opacity of the suspension has markedly diminished and after 24 hours the previously opaque suspension will have become almost clear.

INFLUENCE OF THE MEDIUM ON THE ANTI-BACTERIAL TITRE OF THE MOULD CULTURE

So far as has been ascertained nutrient broth is the most suitable medium for the production of penicillin. The addition of glucose or saccharose, which are fermented by the mould with the production of acid, delays or prevents the appearance of the antibacterial substance. Dilution of the broth with water delays the formation of the antibacterial substance and diminishes the concentration which is ultimately reached.

Inhibitory Power of Penicillin on the Growth of Bacteria

Tables 2 and 3 show the extent to which various microbes, pathogenic and non-pathogenic, are inhibited by penicillin. The first table shows the inhibition by the agar plate method and the second shows the inhibitory power when diluted in nutrient broth.

Certain interesting facts emerge from these tables. It is clear that penicillin contains bacterio-inhibitory substance which is very active towards some microbes while not affecting others. The members of the coli-typhoid group are unaffected as are other intestinal bacilli such as B. pyocyaneus, B. proteus and V. cholerae. Other bacteria which are insensitive to penicillin are the enterococcus, some of the Gram-negative cocci of the mouth, Friedländer's pneumobacillus, and B. influenzae (Pfeiffer), while the action on B. dysenteriae (Flexner), and B. pseudo-tuberculosis rodentium is almost negligible. The anthrax bacillus is completely inhibited in a 1 in 10 dilution but in this case the inhibitory influence is trifling when compared with the effect on the pyogenic cocci.

It is on the pyogenic cocci and on bacilli of the diphtheria group that the action is most manifest.

Staphylococci are very sensitive, and the inhibitory effect is practically the same on all strains, whatever the colour or type of the staphylococcus.

Streptococcus pyogenes is also very sensitive. There were small differences in the titre with different strains, but it may be said generally that it is slightly more sensitive than staphylococcus.

TABLE 2. Inhibitory Power of Penicillin (Heated and Unheated) on Various Microbes (Agar Plate Method).

Type of microbe.	Extent of inhibition in mm. from penicillin embedded in agar, serum agar, or blood agar plates.		
	Unheated.		Boiled for 1 minute.
Experiment 1:			
Staphylococcus pyogenes	23	.	21
Streptococcus pyogenes	17	.	17
Streptococcus viridans (mouth)	17	.	15
Diphtheroid bacillus	27	.	22
Sarcina	10	.	10
Micrococcus lysodeikticus	6	.	7
Micrococcus from air (1)	20	.	16
Micrococcus from air (2)	4	.	9
B. anthracis	0	.	0
B. typhosus	0	.	0
Enterococcus	0	.	0
Experiment 2:			
Staphylococcus pyogenes	24	.	...
Streptococcus pyogenes	30	.	...
Streptococcus viridans (mouth)	25	.	...
Pneumococcus	30	.	...
Diphtheroid bacillus	35	.	...
B. pyocyaneus	0	.	...
B. pneumoniae (Friedlander)	0	.	...
B. coli	0	.	...
B. paratyphosus A	0	.	...
Experiment 3:			
Staphylococcus pyogenes	16	.	...
Gonococcus	16	.	...
Meningococcus	17	.	...
Experiment 4:			
Staphylococcus pyogenes	17	.	...
Staphylococcus epidermidis	18	.	...
Streptococcus pyogenes	15	.	...
Streptococcus viridans (faeces)	5	.	...
B. diphtheriae (2 strains)	14	.	...
Diphtheroid bacillus	10	.	...
Gram-negative coccus from the mouth (1)	12	.	...
Gram-negative coccus from the mouth (2)	0	.	...
B. coli	0	.	...
B. influenzae (Pfeiffer) 6 strains	0	.	...

TABLE 3. Inhibitory Power of Penicillin on Different Bacteria.

	Dilution of penicillin in broth.											
	1/5.	1/10.	1/20.	1/40.	1/80.	1/100.	1/200.	1/400.	1/800.	1/1600.	1/3200.	Control.
Staphylococcus aureus	0	0	0	0	0	0	0	0	±	++	++	++
Staphylococcus epidermidis	0	0	0	0	0	0	0	0	±	++	++	++
Pneumococcus	0	0	0	0	0	0	0	0	0	++	++	++
Streptococcus (haemolytic)	0	0	0	0	0	0	0	0	0	±	++	++
Streptococcus viridans (mouth)	0	0	0	0	0	0	±	++	++	++	++	++
Streptococcus faecalis	++	++	++	++	++	++	++	++	++	++	++	++
B. anthracis	0	0	+	+	++	++	++	++	++	++	++	++
B. pseudo-tuberculosis rodentium	+	+	++	++	++	++	++	++	++	++	++	++
B. pullorum	+	+	++	++	++	++	++	++	++	++	++	++
B. dysenteriae	+	++	++	++	++	++	++	++	++	++	++	++
B. coli	++	++	++	...	...	...	...	...	...	...	...	...
B. typhosus	++	++	++	...	...	...	...	...	...	...	...	...
B. pyocyaneus	++	++	++	...	...	...	...	...	...	...	...	...
B. proteus	++	++	++	...	...	...	...	...	...	...	...	...
V. cholerae	++	++	++	...	...	...	...	...	...	...	...	...

	1/60.	1/120.	1/300.	1/600.	Control.
B. diphtheriae (3 strains)	0	±	++	++	++
Streptococcus pyogenes (13 strains)	0	0	0	++	++
Streptococcus pyogenes (1 strain)	0	0	±	++	++
Streptococcus faecalis (11 strains)	++	++	++	++	++
Streptococcus viridans at random from faeces (1 strain)	0	0	0	++	++
Streptococcus viridans at random from faeces (2 strains)	0	0	±	++	++
Streptococcus viridans at random from faeces (1 strain)	0	±	++	++	++
Streptococcus viridans at random from faeces (1 strain)	+	++	++	++	++
Streptococcus viridans at random from faeces (1 strain)	++	++	++	++	++
Streptococcus viridans at random from mouth (1 strain)	0	±	++	++	++
Streptococcus viridans at random from mouth (2 strains)	0	0	++	++	++
Streptococcus viridans at random from mouth (1 strain)	0	0	0	++	++

0 = no growth; ± = trace of growth; + = poor growth; + + = normal growth.

Pneumococci are equally sensitive with *Streptococcus pyogenes*.

The green streptococci vary very considerably, a few strains being almost unaffected while others are as sensitive as S. *pyogenes*. Gonococci, meningococci, and some of the Gram-negative cocci found in nasal catarrhal conditions are about as sensitive as are staphylococci. Many of the Gram-negative cocci found in the mouth and throat are, however, quite insensitive.

B. diphteriae is less affected than staphylococcus but is yet completely inhibited by a 1% dilution of a fair sample of penicillin.

It may be noted here that penicillin, which is strongly inhibitory to many bacteria, does not inhibit the growth of the original penicillium which was used in its preparation.

The Rate of Killing of Staphylococci by Penicillin

Some bactericidal agents like the hypochlorites are extremely rapid in their action, others like flavine or novarsenobillon are slow. Experiments were made to find into which category penicillin fell.

To 1 c.c. volumes of dilutions in broth of penicillin were added 10 c.mm. volumes of a 1 in 1000 dilution of a staphylococcus broth culture. The tubes were then incubated at 37°C. and at intervals 10 c.mm. volumes were removed and plated with the following result:

It appears, therefore, that penicillin belongs to the group of slow acting antiseptics, and the staphylococci are only completely killed after an interval of over 4½ hours even in a concentration 30 or 40 times stronger than is necessary to inhibit completely the culture in broth. In the weaker concentrations it will be seen that at first there is growth of the staphylococci and only after some hours are the cocci killed off. The same thing can be seen if a series of dilutions of penicillin in broth are heavily infected with staphylococcus and incubated. If the cultures are examined after four hours it may be seen that growth has taken place apparently equally in all the tubes but when examined after being incubated overnight, the tubes containing penicillin in concentrations greater than 1 in 300 or 1 in 400 are perfectly clear while the control tube shows a heavy growth. This is a clear illustration of the bacteriolytic action of penicillin.

Toxicity of Penicillin

The toxicity to animals of powerfully antibacterial mould broth filtrates appears to be very low. Twenty c.c. injected intravenously into a rabbit were not more toxic than the same quantity of broth. Half a c.c. injected intraperitoneally into a mouse weighing about 20 gm. induced no toxic symptoms. Constant irrigation of large infected surfaces in man was not accompa-

| | Number of colonies developing after sojourn in penicillin in concentrations as under: | | | | |
	Control.	1/80.	1/40.	1/20.	1/10.
Before	27	27	27	27	27
After 2 hours	116	73	51	48	23
After 4½ hours	∞	13	1	2	5
After 8 hours	∞	0	0	0	0
After 12 hours	∞	0	0	0	0

nied by any toxic symptoms, while irrigation of the human conjunctiva every hour for a day had no irritant effect.

In vitro penicillin which completely inhibits the growth of staphylococci in a dilution of 1 in 600 does not interfere with leucocytic function to a greater extent than does ordinary broth.

Use of Penicillin to Demonstrate Other Bacterial Inhibitions

When materials like saliva or sputum are plated it is not uncommon to see, where the implant is thick, an almost pure culture of streptococci and pneumococci, and where the implant is thinner and the streptococcal colonies are more widely separated, other colonies appear, especially those of Gram-negative cocci. These Gram-negative cocci are inhibited by the streptococci (probably by the peroxide they produce in their growth) and it is only when the mass effect of the streptococci is reduced that they appear in the culture.

Penicillin may be used to give a striking demonstration of this inhibition of bacteria by streptococci and pneumococci. Sputum is spread thickly on a culture plate, and then 5 or 6 drops of penicillin is spread over one half of it. After incubation it may be seen that on the half untreated with penicillin there is a confluent growth of streptococci and pneumococci and nothing else, while on the penicillin-treated half many Gram-negative cocci appear which were inhibited by the streptococci and pneumococci, and can only flourish when these are themselves inhibited by the penicillin.

If some active penicillin is embedded in a streak across an agar plate planted with saliva an interesting growth sometimes results. On the portion most distal from the penicillin there are many streptococci, but these are obscured by coarsely growing cocci, so that the resultant growth is a copious confluent rough mass. These coarse growing cocci are extremely penicillin sensitive and stop growing about 25 mm. from the embedded penicillin. Then there is a zone of about 1 cm. wide of pure streptococci, then they are inhibited by the penicillin, and as soon as that happens Gram-negative cocci appear and grow right up to the embedded penicillin. The three zones of growth produced in this way are very striking.

Use of Penicillin in the Isolation of B. Influenzae (Pfeiffer), and Other Organisms

It sometimes happens that in the human body a pathogenic microbe may be difficult to isolate because it occurs in association with others which grow more profusely and which mask it. If in such a case the first microbe is insensitive to penicillin and the obscuring microbes are sensitive, then by the use of this substance these latter can be inhibited while the former are allowed to develop normally. Such an example occurs in the body, certainly with *B. influenzae* (Pfeiffer) and probably with Bordet's whooping-cough bacillus and other organisms. Pfeiffer's bacillus, occurring as it does in the respiratory tract, is usually associated with streptococci, pneumococci, staphylococci and Gram-negative cocci. All of these, with the exception of some of the Gram-negative cocci, are highly sensitive to penicillin and by the addition of some of this to the medium they can be completely inhibited while *B. influenzae* is unaffected. A definite quantity of the penicillin may be incorporated with the molten culture medium before the plates are made, but an easier and very satisfactory method is to spread the infected material, sputum, nasal mucus, etc., on the plate in the usual way and then over one half of the plate spread 2 to 6 drops (according to potency) of the penicillin. This small amount of fluid soaks into the agar and after cultivation for 24 hours it will be found that the half of the plate without the penicillin will show the normal growth while on the penicillin treated half there will be nothing but *B. influenzae* with Gram-negative cocci and occasionally some other microbe. This makes it infinitely easier to isolate these penicillin-insensitive organisms, and repeatedly *B. influenzae* has been isolated in this way when they have not been seen in films of sputum and when it has not been possible to detect them in plates not treated with penicillin. Of course if this method is adopted then a medium favourable for the growth of *B. influenzae* must be used, *e. g.* boiled blood agar, as by the repression of the pneumococci and the staphylococci the symbiotic effect of these, so familiar in cultures of sputum on blood agar, is lost and if blood agar alone is used the colonies of *B. influenzae* may be so minute as to be easily missed.

Figures 2 and 3 are photographs of culture-plates made after the method described above. On the plate shown in figure 2 a mixture of staphylococci and *B. influenzae* was spread over the whole plate of Fildes medium (Fildes, 1921), then 6 drops of penicillin were spread over the lower half of the plate. The upper half shows the mixed culture while the lower half gives a pure culture of *B. influenzae*. Figure 3 represents a culture of nasal mucus from a "cold" made on the same medium. Here, on the upper

half (untreated with penicillin) staphylococci and diphtheroid bacilli grow abundantly, while on the treated (lower) half only some three or four colonies of *B. influenzae* appear. (NOTE: Figures 2-3 not shown.)

In conjunction with my colleague, Dr. McLean, a series of cultures were made from the throats of 25 nurses warded for "influenza." The swabs were planted on boiled blood agar and over half of each plate was spread 3 or 4 drops of penicillin. The results are set forth in table 4.

In the table (p. 40) account has only been taken of the common microbes found in these cultures. In some there were a few diphtheroid bacilli which were always penicillin sensitive, and in others there were Gram-negative bacilli which were penicillin insensitive, although they were inhibited by streptococci or pneumococci. Pneumococci and streptococci were classed together, as complete tests were not made to differentiate one from the other. (From the appearance of the colonies and the morphological characters pneumococci were evidently present in most cases in much larger numbers than were streptococci.)

The swabs were generally planted thickly and in some cases where the growth on the portion of the plate without penicillin was almost confluent, the cultures were sampled by taking smears from thick portions of the growth. In these cases it is possible that the results given do not give a quite complete picture of the cultures. This, however, does not affect the present argument that by the addition of penicillin to the culture medium, and the consequent inhibition of the pyogenic cocci, the isolation of *B. influenzae* is very much easier. And in a number of cases it was isolated when it was completely missed in the cultures without penicillin.

TABLE 4. Summary of Results obtained from Post-Nasal Swabs in
25 Consecutive Cases of "Influenza."

	Without penicillin				With penicillin			
	Pneumococcus or	Streptococcus	B. influenzae	Gram-negative cocci	Pneumococcus or	Streptococcus	B. influenzae	Gram-negative cocci
1.	+	+	+	+	.	−	++	+
2.	+	+	++	++	.	−	++	+
3.	+	+	++	+	.	−	+	−
4.	+	−			.	−	+	+
5.	+	+	−		.	−	++	−
6.	+	+	−		.	−	++	++
7.	+	+	−	++	.	−	+	+
8.	+		+	−	.	−	+	−
9.	+	+	−	−	.	−	+	+
10.	+	+	−	−	.	−	+	−
11.	+	+	−	−	.	−	+	−
12.	+	+	+	++	.	−	++	+
13.	+		++	++	.	−	+	++
14.	+	+	−	−	.	−	+	−
15.	+	+	−	−	.	−	+	+
16.	+	+	−	−	.	−	+	+
17.	+	+	−	−	.	−	+	+
18.	+	+	−	−	.	−	+	+
19.	+	+	+	−	.	−	+	++
20.	+	+	−	−	.	−	−	+
21.	+	+	−	−	.	−	+	+
22.	+	+	−	−	.	−	+	−
23.	+	−	+		.	−	+	+
24.	+	+	++	−	.	−	++	−
25.	+	+	−	++	.	−	−	−

It is quite immaterial how many pneumococci and streptococci are present in a specimen—they are completely inhibited—and even a few *B. influenzae* can be isolated from a mixture with an enormous number of these cocci.

From a number of observations which have been made on sputum, post-nasal and throat swabs it seems likely that by the use of penicillin, organisms of the *B. influenzae* group will be isolated from a great variety of pathological conditions as well as from individuals who are apparently healthy.

Discussion

It has been demonstrated that a species of penicillium produces in culture a very powerful antibacterial substance which affects different bacteria in different degrees. Speaking generally it may be said that the least sensitive bacteria are the Gram-negative bacilli, and the most susceptible are the pyogenic cocci. Inhibitory substances have been described in old cultures of many organisms; generally the inhibition is more or less specific to the microbe which has been used for the culture, and the inhibitory substances are seldom strong enough to withstand even slight dilution with fresh nutrient material. Penicillin is not inhibitory to the original penicillium used in its preparation.

Emmerich and other workers have shown that old cultures of *B. pyocyaneus* acquire a marked bacteriolytic power. The bacteriolytic agent, pyocyanase, possesses properties similar to penicillin in that its heat resistance is the same and it exists in the filtrate of a fluid culture. It resembles penicillin also in that it acts only on certain microbes. It differs however in being relatively extremely weak in its action and in acting on quite different types of bacteria. The bacilli of anthrax, diphtheria, cholera and typhoid are those most sensitive to pyocyanase, while the pyogenic cocci are unaffected, but the percentages of pyocyaneus filtrate necessary for the inhibition of these organisms was 40, 33, 40 and 60 respectively (Bocchia, 1909). This degree of inhibition is hardly comparable with 0.2% or less of penicillin which is necessary to completely inhibit the pyogenic cocci or the 1% necessary for *B. diphtheriae*.

Penicillin, in regard to infections with sensitive microbes, appears to have some advantages over the well-known chemical antiseptics. A good sample will completely inhibit staphylococci, *Streptococcus pyogenes* and pneumococcus in a dilution of 1 in 800. It is therefore a more powerful inhibitory agent than is carbolic acid and it can be applied to an infected surface undiluted as it is non-irritant and non-toxic. If applied, therefore, on a dressing, it will still be effective even when diluted 800 times which is more than can be said of the chemical antiseptics in use. Experiments in connection with its value in the treatment of pyogenic infections are in progress.

In addition to its possible use in the treatment of bacterial infections penicillin is certainly useful to the bacteriologist for its power of inhibiting unwanted microbes in bacterial cultures so that penicillin insensitive bacteria can readily be isolated. A notable instance of this is the very easy isolation of Pfeiffer's bacillus of influenza when penicillin is used.

In conclusion my thanks are due to my colleagues, Mr. Ridley and Mr. Craddock, for their help in carrying out some of the experiments described in this paper, and to our mycologist, Mr. la Touche, for his suggestions as to the identity of the penicillium.

Summary

1. A certain type of penicillium produces in culture a powerful antibacterial substance. The antibacterial power of the culture reaches its maximum in about 7 days at 20° C. and after 10 days diminishes until it has almost disappeared in 4 weeks.

2. The best medium found for the production of the antibacterial substance has been ordinary nutrient broth.

3. The active agent is readily filterable and the name "penicillin" has been given to filtrates of broth cultures of the mould.

4. Penicillin loses most of its power after 10 to 14 days at room temperature but can be preserved longer by neutralization.

5. The active agent is not destroyed by boiling for a few minutes but in alkaline solution boiling for 1 hour markedly reduces the power. Autoclaving for 20 minutes at 115° C. practically destroys it. It is soluble in alcohol but insoluble in ether or chloroform.

6. The action is very marked on the pyogenic cocci and the diphtheria group of bacilli. Many bacteria are quite insensitive, *e.g.* the coli-typhoid group, the influenza-bacillus group, and the enterococcus.

7. Penicillin is non-toxic to animals in enormous doses and is non-irritant. It does not interfere with leucocytic function to a greater degree than does ordinary broth.

8. It is suggested that it may be an efficient antiseptic for application to, or injection into, areas infected with penicillin-sensitive microbes.

9. The use of penicillin on culture plates renders obvious many bacterial inhibitions which are not very evident in ordinary cultures.

10. Its value as an aid to the isolation of *B. influenzae* has been demonstrated.

VII

I N AN AGE OF ever-increasing specialization in science, **ecology** attempts to look at the complex life system as a whole. Briefly, ecology may be defined as the study of the complex network of interrelationships among living organisms, plant and animal, and their environment. Environment may be defined as the sum of all forces or conditions acting on an organism or a community of organisms.

In "The New Ecology," Eugene P. Odum pleads for a bringing together of the widely divergent roots of ecology. A promising path to this goal, he points out, is a shift in emphasis from the descriptive to the functional. Studies on energetics, nutrient cycling, species diversity, functional niches, ecological regulation, etc., accompanied by improved analytical, mathematical and experimental procedures are bringing out denominations of function.

Even more fundamental in bringing together all ecologists, Odum believes, is the ecosystem, the basic unit of structure and function with which ecologists must deal. Ecologists can rally round the ecosystem as their basic unit just as molecular biologists now rally round the cell. The new ecology is thus a systems ecology—dealing with the structure and function of levels of organization beyond that of the individual and the species.

In conclusion, Odum urges biology departments in our colleges to review their curricula to make certain they are offering their students adequate exposure to the new ecology.

The New Ecology

From Eugene P. Odum, "The New Ecology," *Bio-Science*, Vol. 14, No. 7 (July 1964), pp. 14-16. Reprinted by permission of the author and the American Institute of Biological Sciences.

GRANTING THAT the subject matter and general aims of ecology as a branch of biology have remained unchanged for a century or more, the field has nevertheless recently achieved a maturity, a cohesiveness, and an importance in human affairs that is new. The new ecology is rooted in a solid historical development, but its rise to a front-line position in man's thinking is a consequence of the exploitation of atomic energy, the exploration of outer space, and the human population explosion. Thus, both historical perspectives and modern pressures need to be considered if we are to understand the new dimensions and, especially, if we are to meet the challenges posed by problems of man and his environment.

In an earlier essay (*ASB Bulletin*, 4:27-29, 1957), I singled out as being important in the development of present-day ecology several roots that go back into the early history of biology. One deep root goes back to the old "natural philosophy" and the more recent natural history, and it leads to modern research on ecological life histories. Another important root starts with the early studies of the physical factors of the environment, progresses through the idea of limiting factors stemming from Liebig, and leads into the modern studies of microenvironments and physiological ecology. Still another root begins with Malthus, Verhulst, Lotka, Pearl, and other demographers and leads to the very active field of population ecology. The beginnings of another root may be found in the studies of Mobius, Warming, Cowles, Elton, Clements, and Shelford at the community level. Finally, from aquatic biology comes another important root springing from the thinking of Forbes, Thienemann, Hutchinson, Lindeman and many others leading to studies of tropho-dynamics, bioenergetics, and biogeochemical cycles. Until quite recently, these widely divergent approaches remained largely separate fields with little general theory to connect them. Worst of all, specialists have too often attempted to extend narrow approaches into 'general theories' that differ as widely as do the approaches, much to the confusion of those who look for some kind of unity of thinking among ecologists that might be comparable, for example, with that found among geneticists.

The levels-of-organization concept, which is not new but which has only recently achieved wide acceptance by biologists, has played an important part in uniting these diverse roots into something resembling a trunk of central ecological theory. Inherent in this concept is the theory that homeostasis, or biological regulation, is equally important at all levels in the spectrum from molecules to ecosystems. This means that functions and principles change as smaller units are integrated into a larger one. Therefore, structure and function at any one level explains *only in part* the structure and function at another level which itself must also be studied to complete the picture. Thus, ecology is not an extension of biochemistry or physiology, as many seem to believe, but is a basic division of biology that requires direct scientific attention as do other divisions. It is extremely important that all major levels of organization receive our best efforts in both teaching and research if we are to have the kind of feedback necessary for a real understanding of the complex world in which we live.

A shift in emphasis from the descriptive to the functional has also been very important in bringing together the widely divergent roots of ecology. As long as a purely descriptive approach was emphasized, there was little in common between the sea and the forest or between higher plants and higher animals and, therefore, little exchange of ideas between marine and terrestrial ecologists or between plant and animal ecologists. Now, however, studies on energetics, nutrient cycling, species diversity, functional niches, ecological regulation, etc., accompanied by improved analytical, mathematical, and experimental procedures, are bringing out common denominators of function. It is important to note that many functional principles, such as those relating to the laws of thermodynamics or to metabolism, are the same at all levels of organization, but structure is vastly different at different levels. Therefore, the real difference between levels lies in the interaction of similar functions with differing structures. For example, the biochemical nature of photosynthesis may be the same in a cell as in a forest, but the structure of a forest is so vastly different from the structure of a cell that studies at the cell level do not explain energy fixation, homeostasis, survival, and evolution of the forest.

In my opinion, the ecosystem concept brings together all ecologists, because the ecosystem is the basic unit of structure and function with which we must ultimately deal. Ecologists can rally around the ecosystem as their basic unit just as molecular biologists now rally around the cell, another important basic unit of structure and function. *The new ecology is thus a systems ecology*—or, to put it in other words, the new ecology deals with the structure and function of levels of organization beyond that of the individual and species. Or we might say that ecology is the study of the structure and function of nature, if we define nature as any life-support system (i.e., any ecosystem) functioning within whatever space we chose to consider whether it be a culture vessel, a space capsule, a crop field, a pond, or the earth's biosphere.

If my experience in lecturing along the above lines is a guide, I shall predict that my readers are now divided into two camps. One group may be thinking "all of this is obvious, quite axiomatic in fact; any school child knows that the whole is not a sum of the parts." The other group remains unconvinced that there is anything really new or different at ecological levels that can not be ultimately explained either by the reduction of the whole into even smaller parts or by expanding knowledge gleaned from parts directly to the whole. Hoping to make some impression on group 2 without boring group 1, I usually resort to examples at about this point in the presentation.

Regulation at any level requires communication of some sort. At the cell level, communication is largely or entirely across or within living protoplasm, with the "messengers" being complex organic substances, the enzymes. In sharp contrast, coordination at ecological levels involves communication across non-living space. Thus, I am now communicating with the reader across the non-living printed page (and hoping for some feedback!). While complex biochemicals may also serve as "messengers" in the ecosystem (i.e., "environmental hormones"), regulation is often accomplished by entirely different and, oftentimes, simpler mechanisms. In territorial birds, for example, relatively simple sound waves of song provide the mechanism. In this case, the mechanism regulating population size is quite different and, from a physio-chemical standpoint, less complex than the mechanism regulating cell size; neither mechanism could have been predicted from the study of the other. The field of behavior, which is experiencing a considerable revival that is closely tied in with the new ecology, is studyable only at the level of the organism and beyond. At least, if anyone thinks that bird or human behavior can be understood by reducing the population to macromolecules, I would like to learn how this might be done. For more about the shortcomings of the "reductionist philosophy," see the essay by Dubos in the January 1964 issue of *BioScience*.

Another important difference between cells and ecosystems lies in the fact that species diversity is important in the function of the latter but nonexistent in the former (where function, of course, is limited by the genetic material of a single species or strain). Many of the unique properties of the ecosystem, such as its ability to regulate the physical environment (CO_2 level in air, for example), result from the interaction of species. The most intimate cooperation in terms of efficient feedback often involves species of widely divergent genetics such as plants and animals in the biosphere, corals and algae on a reef, fungi and algae in lichens, or man and wheat in agriculture. Again, there should be lots of exchange between the physiologist who need work only with one species at a time ("pure culture") and the ecologist who must ultimately work with interacting species ("mixed cultures"), but neither work is a substitute for the other.

When I was a graduate student, even ecologists tended to ignore the diversity of nature in order to concentrate study on a few "dominant" species. While only a few species often account for 99% of the energy flow at any one point in time and space, it is now becoming evident that the many rare species so characteristic of nature are important from the standpoint of long-term adaptation and stability. The question of diversity in nature is a particularly important one because man's theory of environmental management, at least up to the present time, is that reduced diversity leads to greater control of nature for the benefit of man. Nature's theory, if the reader will pardon the teleology, seems to hold that diversification results in greater biological control and stabilization of the environment. Both theories are probably valid, but at different levels and for different sizes of ecosystem. Clarification of these relationships is important for the future, because man could easily go too far in acting on a principle that may hold at one level but not at another. In this important area of study, the new ecology draws closer to the new taxonomy and the new evolution which are also becoming functional as well as descriptive.

Increasing interest in theoretical models is a sure sign that ecology is approaching greater maturity and unity. While the accomplishments of the theoretical ecologist have not been spectacular so far, we may confidently expect that he will play an increasingly important role in the future development of the field. Both the mathematical model and the analogue-computer approach appear promising. MacArthur,

Slobodkin, K. Watt, Nicholson, Margalef, and Patten are among those attempting to set up models for ecological processes on the basis of differential equations, information theory, or other mathematical concepts, while Howard T. Odum is a pioneer in the use of electrical analogue circuitry as a model for the ecosystem (see *American Scientist*, 48:1-8, 1960). Since ecological structure is readily shown in a diagram but difficult to depict in the language of pure mathematics, the electrical analogue circuit diagram or working model has the advantage of simplicity in relating structure and function. The flow-chart models are also much easier to understand for most of us who are not skilled in higher mathematics.

We need dwell but briefly on the atomic age pressures mentioned in the first paragraph of this essay, because all mankind is acutely aware of the environment problems related to fallout, the threat of nuclear war, pollution, pest control, overpopulation, and the design of life-support systems for space travel. Each of these aspects deserves a more lengthy treatment than can be accorded in this paper; good summary papers and symposia are now beginning to appear in the literature. We can only hope that ecology is not too little and too late to provide its fair share of basic information needed to solve the problems. The net result of the atomic age should be favorable if new tools, such as radioactive tracers, and new thinking about the minimum ecosystem for man in space can be fully exploited in terms of man's continued survival in the biosphere. I have been personally disappointed in the slowness of ecologists to take advantage of the new opportunities despite efforts to beef up post-doctoral training. Ecologists who are willing or able to be retrained are fewer than expected. Therefore, attention must be turned to the training of pre-doctoral students and the recruiting of investigators from the more crowded areas of the biological spectrum. One bottleneck has been that traditional biology courses and texts contain little or no ecology. The new paperback series and some of the new high school texts are succeeding in some measure in bringing to the student and citizen some of the excitement of the new ecology. In my opinion, some of our best universities are falling down on the job very badly. It is a sad situation when the University of Georgia, a relatively small university and recent entry into graduate training, turns out to have a larger program in ecology (in terms of staff, graduate students, and experimental field facilities) than is supported by many of our finest prestige universities that traditionally attract the best brains. I sincerely beg all heads of biology departments who may read this article to take stock of their situation to see if all of the biological spectrum is being adequately supported by teaching and research in their departments.

If biologists do not rise to the challenge, who will advise on the management of man's environment—the technicians who have great skill but no understanding, or the politicians who have neither?

VIII

ALBERT SCHWEITZER remarked in his autobiography that "the great fault of all ethics hitherto has been that they believed themselves to have to deal only with the relations of man to man."

In the following article, Marston Bates argues eloquently that ethics must also consider man's relationship to nature. More and more, in all areas, we have tended to separate the study of man from the study of nature. The natural sciences and the social sciences exist in practically complete isolation from one another.

Now, in this time of ecological crisis, the philosopher, the biologist and the social scientist must, says Mr. Bates, be concerned with man's relationship to nature. Believing that man must make every effort to maintain diversity in nature, Mr. Bates sorts out the arguments for his position into those that are primarily ethical, those that are aesthetic and those that are utilitarian. The result is a thoughtful and positive statement on how man can share life rather than destroy it.

Man's Place in Nature

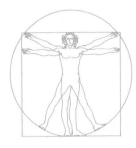

WE STARTED this book in the tropical forest, thinking about the sea, looking at the similarities in the way life is organized in these different circumstances. This led us to some reflections on the continuity of life in space, in the biosphere, and on its continuity in time, in evolution. The grand design of this system of life includes many different patterns—seas, reefs, lakes, rivers, forests, grasslands and deserts—and we looked at some of these. The structure of the system is everywhere similar, though everywhere complex, turning on the relations among individuals, populations and communities of organisms, and on relations with the physical environment. We have only glanced at these relations, though I hope the glance has been lingering enough to reveal some of the infinite possibilities for study and contemplation.

Then we came to man and his place in this system of life. We could have left man out, playing the ecological game of "let's pretend man doesn't exist." But this seems as unfair as the corresponding game of the economists, "let's pretend nature doesn't exist." The economy of nature and the ecology of man are inseparable and attempts to separate them are more than misleading, they are dangerous. Man's destiny is tied to nature's destiny and the arrogance of the engineering mind does not change this. Man may be a very peculiar animal, but he is still a part of the system of nature.

From the point of view of zoological classification, man is easy enough to deal with. To be sure, there are all sorts of variations among men in color of skin, eyes and hair; in texture of hair and in its distribution over the body; in details of the face and bodily physique. But no special study is needed to show that these varieties breed together easily and freely whenever they come in contact: that they form a single species.

The classification of the varieties does present problems. They can be lumped together into three or four main types, or they can be split into thirty or forty different races. Whatever system is used, many individuals will be found that do not fit into any category. The varieties, however, show a rough geographical pattern and it is likely that the differences arose through geographical separation, a common enough phenomenon with many kinds of animals.

This human species, as I pointed out, can logically be placed in a genus and family by itself; and men, along with the great apes, Old World monkeys, New World monkeys and a few other animals, can be grouped as an order (the primates) in the general class of mammals.

From the point of view of ecology, man is less easy to deal with. Essentially he is a predatory animal, a second- or third-order consumer. But he shows a tremendous variety of food habits and in many parts of the world he is primarily a first-order consumer, living directly off vegetation. This is probably a rather recent development (in geological terms) because man's plant-eating habits depend to a large degree on processing with fire. The tubers and grains that make up the basic starches of the human diet in most parts of the world are inedible for man unless cooked. He can and does, on the other hand, eat meat of all sorts

(including fish and molluscs) without cooking. His vegetable diet, without fire, would be limited to things like fruits and nuts.

It is hard to define the human habitat, because men are found everywhere on land and around the margins of the seas, except under conditions of extreme dryness or extreme cold. But this wide ecological distribution depends on cultural rather than biological traits: on the use of fire, the wearing of clothes, the construction of shelters, the management of boats. It looks as though naked, uncultured man would be a tropical or subtropical species adapted to the rain forest or to transition zones between forest and scrub or forest and grassland. But we have no specimens of uncultured man for study.

When we try to study the relations of man with the physical and biological environment, we always come up against the problem of how to deal with cultural traits. Should we consider culture as a part of man, as an essential attribute of the human species; or should we consider culture as a part of the environment in which this human species lives? This seems like a quibbling, academic sort of question, but it has worried me for a long time. And this specific and striking case has contributed to my general feeling that it is often misleading to attempt to distinguish sharply between organism and environment, whether dealing with men or mice. We are always concerned with interacting systems—which sometimes act as single systems.

I have no substitute for the idea of environment, and I wouldn't know how to get along without the word, but it is tricky. To get back to the problem of man: it seems to me that in general, psychologists tend to treat culture as a part of the environment, while anthropologists tend to regard culture as a part of man, as a part of his equipment for dealing with the environment. To put it another way, psychologists tend to regard culture as a constant, something to which all men are subjected, and they are interested in the ways in which individuals cope with this: how they learn to conform or, consciously or unconsciously, to rebel. They find that frustrations, joys, neuroses, psychoses, all sorts of human behavioral patterns, derive from the interactions between animal man and this cultural environment. At least it often seems to me that this is what they are doing—though the psychologists themselves are not particularly apt to use the word culture.

In contrast, anthropologists tend to take "human nature" for granted, to regard animal man as more or less the same everywhere and to explain all differences in cultural terms. They find culture to be adaptive: the Eskimo way of life fitted to the arctic and subarctic environment, the Dyak way of life to the rain forest conditions of Borneo. They are preoccupied with the description and analysis of all the different kinds of culture they can find, with the study of cultural evolution, and with the effects of cultural diffusion and contact.

In its extreme form, this point of view in anthropology ignores animal man altogether. Culture, I suppose they would have to admit, could not continue without continuing men, and men in this sense created the cultural forces. But men have long since become the helpless victims of their cultures, and developments go on inexorably, according to the laws governing cultural evolution, regardless of the will or desire or power of any individual.

From the point of view of biology, it is most convenient to treat culture sometimes as an attribute of man, sometimes as a part of human environment. The biologist, trying to look at the human species, cannot think in terms of man and environment: he must deal always with man-culture-environment. Pygmies in the Congo, Bantu in the Congo, Belgians in the Congo, are all men, *Homo sapiens*, in a particular geographical and ecological environment. But they behave quite differently; the environment has quite different meanings for them; they, in turn, have quite different effects on the environment. The whole ecological situation is different.

The problem of man's place in nature, then, is the problem of the relations between man's developing cultures and other aspects of the biosphere. The understanding of these is greatly handicapped by the way in which we have come to organize knowledge. To be sure, man with his varying cultures and cultural traits forms a special phenomenon which requires special means of study and the accumulation of special sorts of information. But still, man has not escaped from the biosphere. He has got into a new, unprecedented kind of relationship with the biosphere; and his success in maintaining this may well depend not only on his understanding of himself, but on his understanding of this world in which he lives.

This makes the split between the social and biological sciences particularly unfortunate. Economics and ecology, as words, have the same root; but that is about all they have in common. As fields of knowledge, they are cultivated in remotely separated parts of our universities, through the use of quite different methods, by scholars who would hardly recognize anything in common. The world of the ecologists is "unspoiled nature." They tend to avoid cities, parks, fields, orchards. The real world of the economists is like Plato's, it is a world of ideas, of abstractions—money, labor, market, goods, capital. There is no room for squirrels scolding in the oak trees, no room for robins on the lawn. There is no room for people either, for that matter—people loving and hating and dreaming. People become the labor force or the market.

More and more, in all areas, we tend to separate the study of man from the study of nature. The separation is one of the basic lines of division in the way we have organized knowledge, in our pattern of specialization. The natural sciences and the social sciences exist in practically complete isolation from one another. Man's body, curiously, has been left with the natural sciences while the social sciences have taken over his mind—at a time when we are most aware of the artificiality of the body-mind separation.

Our third great division of basic knowledge, the humanities, has long since forgotten about nature. Joseph Wood Krutch can well remark: "There are many courses in 'The Nature Poets' in American colleges. But nature is usually left out of them." Surely there is some way of putting all of these things together, of achieving a more balanced view of ourselves and the rest of the natural world. The matter, I think, has some urgency.

Ours has been aptly called the age of anxiety, and this is curious. We should be able to look about us and feel a certain self-satisfaction. We have learned to develop and direct tremendous power; we can create the

kind of conditions we find comfortable; we can produce large quantities of a great variety of foods; we have achieved a surprising degree of control over disease and physical pain. In almost any way we assess man's relations with his environment, he seems to be doing well when compared with the past, even though there is still obvious room for great improvement.

Yet, despite this abundance and progress, almost all attempts to look at man's future are gloomy. I can't think of any recently written image of the future that sounds very attractive, even when the author was trying hard to look for glories. The glories mostly turn out to be bigger and better gadgets, faster trips to a dismal Mars, or better adjusted husbands and wives who no longer take to drink. Usually the author looking into the future doesn't pretend to like his 1984 or his brave new world: but looking about him, this is what he sees coming.

Our anxiety about the future, when we analyze it, turns largely on three related things: the likelihood of continuing warfare, the dizzy rate of human population growth, and the exhaustion of resources. But these don't look like insoluble problems. Surely men who can manufacture a moon can learn to stop killing each other; men who can control infectious disease can learn to breed more thoughtfully than guinea pigs; men who can measure the universe can learn to act wisely in handling the materials of the universe. Why are we so pessimistic?

Chiefly, I suspect, because we have come more and more to doubt our ability to act rationally. Reason seems to be a property of individual men, not of the species or of organized groups. Somewhere we have lost the faith of the Eighteenth Century French philosophers in the perfectibility of man, and the rather different faith of the Nineteenth Century in the idea of progress.

Maybe the anthropologists are right when they say that culture acts as a thing in itself, sweeping along according to inexorable laws, no more under man's control than rodent evolution is under the control of the mice in the fields. The difference between men and mice, then, would be a matter only of awareness, of self-consciousness. We can study the laws of cultural evolution—or organic evolution—but we can't change them. We can foretell our doom but we can't forestall it.

I don't believe this, and I doubt whether the extreme culturists really believe it either. If they believed what they say, I think they wouldn't talk so much. They are like the disciples of Karl Marx who say they believe in the inexorable dialectic of history, but continually try to give history a push in the right direction. Man can't change the laws of cultural evolution or organic evolution—true enough, no doubt—but understanding the laws and acting with the laws, he can influence the consequences. He has in his hands a certain measure of control over his destiny, but this control depends on understanding, and on the spread and proper use of knowledge.

The great immediate threat, of course, is the misuse of nuclear power, the danger of catastrophic war. The long-term threat is the cancerous multiplication of the numbers of men: a new human population the size of the city of Detroit every month, year after year. The thought is dizzying. And then the thought of a nuclear blast capable of killing last month's millions in a few seconds is hardly reassuring.

It looks as though, as a part of nature, we have become a disease of nature—perhaps a fatal disease. And when the host dies, so does the pathogen.

How, in the face of our power, in the face of our danger, do we develop a guiding philosophy?

No single man, no single field of knowledge, holds the answer to that. But all men and all knowledge can contribute to the answer. Insofar as man's relations with the rest of nature are concerned, I think we must make every effort to maintain diversity—that we must make this effort even though it requires constant compromise with apparent immediate needs. To look at this, it may be most convenient to sort out the arguments into those that are primarily ethical, those that are primarily esthetic, and those that are essentially utilitarian.

Albert Schweitzer remarks in his autobiography that "the great fault of all ethics hitherto has been that they believed themselves to have to deal only with the relations of man to man." This is particularly true in the Western, Christian tradition. The present material world, in the philosophy of this tradition, is unimportant, no more than a transient scene for the testing of the soul's fitness for eternity. The material universe is completely man-centered. Nature, insofar as it is noticed, is only a convenience—or a temptation—with no positive value in itself.

Animals are unimportant because they have no souls. God may notice the sparrows, but this is an example of His omniscience rather than of His preoccupation. Even Christ gave no thought to the Gadarene swine. The first arguments against bear-baiting, cockfighting and the like were not that they were liable to cause injury and pain to the animals, but that they were liable to demoralize the human character, leading to gambling, thievery and the like.

For a considerable part of humanity, however, this world has direct religious significance. Many primitive religions have various forms of nature worship, of animism and totemism. But in some of the great religions, particularly Buddhism and Hinduism, attitudes toward nature—toward animals in particular—have an ethical basis. For many millions of Hindus it is a sin to kill any animal. With the Jains, this is carried to an extreme to avoid possible injury even to the tiniest of insects.

We deplore the Hindu attitude toward cattle as uneconomical—which it certainly is—and a handicap to the development of India. In countries within the Western tradition, however, attitudes toward animals often cannot be explained on practical or rational grounds. I suspect that a visitor from Mars, observing our treatment of dogs, cats and other domestic pets, would conclude that they were sacred animals. Horses in some Western subcultures are also treated as sacred animals. The horror of eating horse meat—or dog meat—seems not too different from the Muslim horror of eating pig or the Hindu horror of eating any animal.

There have always been individuals within the Christian tradition with a love of nature, with a kind feeling toward animals. St. Francis of Assisi rightfully is their patron. In modern times this has grown into a cult of great emotional force, leading to the development of a variety of formal organizations for the prevention of cruelty to animals, for the protection of wildlife, which reaches an extreme in the antivivisectionist groups. This attitude is most highly developed in the industrialized regions since it goes along with economic security and relative leisure. It is a characteristic of "affluent societies." It is reassuring in the sense that kindness and tolerance and sympathy—whether for slaves, for children or for animals—seem to gain force and spread with economic development.

This kindness and sympathy for animals might well be classed as an ethical attitude. Curiously, along with the cult of kindness to animals, we have a parallel development in the same societies and circumstances of the cult of the sportsman, in which killing becomes a good in itself. As hunting ceased to be a necessity, it became a luxury for men; and hunting as play, hunting as sport, has long characterized classes of men with the leisure to indulge in it. Hunting is sometimes thought to represent a basic "instinct" in human nature, and certainly there is something elemental and primitive in the thrill of the chase. Intellectually, I have abandoned hunting as a sport since, when a boy, I watched the agonies of a raccoon I had wounded. But often enough, hunting for some worthy "scientific" purpose, I have felt my intellectual pretensions slide away and I have become lost in the purely emotional absorption of getting my game.

The sport of kings and noblemen has now become the sport of millions, of anyone with an automobile and a rifle or shotgun. It is recreation. But also a philosophy has developed whereby this killing of deer and ducks and quail is supposed to inculcate virtue. Krutch quotes the propaganda slogan of a gun company: "Go hunting with your boy and you'll never have to go hunting for him."

I get lost in the ethical issues involved in these problems. Intellectually I sympathize with the teachings of Buddha, that all life is sacred. But practically, I see no way of acting on this. There is no logical stopping place before the end reached by the people of Samuel Butler's *Erewhon*. They became vegetarian out of respect for the rights of animals. But as one of their learned men pointed out, vegetables are equally alive, and equally have rights. So the Erewhonians, to be consistent, are reduced to eating cabbages certified to have died a natural death. Monkeys, deer, cows, rats, quail, songbirds, lizards, fish, insects, molluscs, vegetables—where do you draw the line between what can be properly killed and eaten, and what not? It so happens that I don't like decayed cabbages and I do like rare roast beef—which leaves me, as usual, blundering around in a quandary.

The ethical question is difficult. We have drifted in the modern world into a position of ethical relativism which leaves us with no absolutes of good and bad, right and wrong. Things are good or right according to the context, depending on the values of the society or culture. Yet one feels that there must be some basis of right conduct, applicable to all men and all places and not depending on any particular dogma or any specific revelation. Science has undermined the dogmas and revelations; and it provides, for many working scientists, a sort of faith, a sort of humanism, that can replace the need for an articulated code of conduct. But our scientists and philosophers have so far failed to explain this in a way that reaches any very large number of people. This, it seems to me, is one of the great tasks of modern philosophy, which the philosophers, dallying in their academic groves, have shunned.

When some thinker does come forth to provide us with a rationale for conduct, he will have to consider not only the problems of man's conduct with his fellow men, but also of man's conduct toward nature. Life is a unity; the biosphere is a complex network of interrelations among all the host of living things. Man, in gaining the godlike quality of awareness, has also acquired a godlike responsibility. The questions of the nature of his relationships with the birds and the beasts, with the trees of the forests and the fish of the seas, become ethical questions: questions of what is good and right not only for man himself, but for the living world as a whole. In the words of Aldo Leopold, we need to develop an ecological conscience.

It is sometimes said that the esthetic appreciation of nature is relatively new, that the Greeks, for instance, did not admire landscapes. The matter can be argued and I don't know that anyone has made a careful study of changing attitudes, or of differences in attitude among the great civilizations. Within our own civilization, it looks as though the conscious appreciation of the beauties of nature had its roots in the so-called Romantic Movement of the Eighteenth Century. We can see this most plainly in literature, in landscape painting and in landscape architecture. It is less clear in the other arts, though Lovejoy plausibly equates it with the love of diversity and the search for new forms that characterize Western art generally in the last two centuries.

It looks as though man's esthetic appreciation of nature increases as the development of his civilization removes him from constant and immediate contact with nature. The peasant hardly notices the grandeur of the view from his fields; the woodsman is not impressed by stately trees, nor the fisherman by the forms and colors on the reefs. In part, this is the general problem of not seeing the familiar, of not appreciating what we have until it is lost.

The reasons behind the conservation movement, from this point of view, are similar to the reasons for preserving antiquities, for maintaining museums of art or history or science. Nature is beautiful, therefore it should not be wantonly destroyed. Representative landscapes should be preserved because of their esthetic value, because of their importance in scientific study, and because of their possibilities for recreation.

I have often wished, as I saw a tropical forest being cleared, that this beautiful place could somehow be protected and preserved for the future to enjoy. The idea, to the people involved in the clearing, seems absurd. The forest is an enemy, to be fought and destroyed; beauty lies in the fields and orchards that will replace it. This was the attitude of our ancestors who in the end effectively cleared the great deciduous forest that once covered the eastern United States, leaving only accidental and incidental traces. How we would love now to have a fair sample of that great forest! But the idea of deliberately saving a part of the wilderness they were conquering never occurred to the pioneers. Nor does it occur to pioneers now in parts of the world where pioneering is still possible.

There must be some way in which one nation can profit by the experience of another nation; some way of saving examples of the landscapes and wildlife that have not yet been devastated by the onrush of industrial civilization. In Africa there is a danger that the national parks will be regarded as toys of colonial administrations, and fade with the fading of those administrations. And the colonial powers, even with the experience of loss in their homelands, are not always too careful about the preservation and maintenance of samples of the natural world under their care.

In tropical America we have the effect of the Spanish tradition. The Romantic Movement never crossed the Pyrenees. Spanish thought and art remain essentially man-centered. Some of my Spanish friends have suggested that the relative failure of science to develop in that tradition may be a consequence of this indifference, on the part of most of the people, to the world of nature. The correction for this might be deliberate attempts to foster nature study in the school systems. Whatever the cause, the conservation movement has not made great headway in the parts of the world dominated by Spanish culture.

In the United States, we have a National Park system, and various sorts of reservations and wildlife refuges under national, state and private auspices. This is largely the consequence of the dedicated efforts of a few people, and we are still far from the point where we can sit back and congratulate ourselves. Conservation interests fall under different branches of government and efforts to form a coherent and unified national policy have not been very successful; we still have no Department of Conservation with cabinet rank. The struggle for financial support is always hard. And there is a constant, eroding pressure from conflicting private and governmental interests.

Ugliness—by any esthetic standard—remains the predominant characteristic of development, of urbanization, of industrialization. We talk about regional planning, diversification, working with the landscape

—and we build vast stretches of the new suburbia. The ideas so forcefully developed by Patrick Geddes, Lewis Mumford and others like them, fall on deaf ears. We need an ecological conscience. We also need to develop ecological appreciation. The Romantic Movement, despite its two hundred year history, has not yet reached our city councils or our highway engineers.

Practical considerations are—and perhaps ought to be—overwhelmingly important in governing man's relations with the rest of nature. Utility, at first thought, requires man to concentrate selfishly and arrogantly on his own immediate needs and convenience, to regard nature purely as a subject for exploitation. A little further thought, however, shows the fallacy of this. The danger of complete man-centeredness in relation to nature is like the danger of immediate and thoughtless selfishness everywhere: the momentary gain results in ultimate loss and defeat. "Enlightened self-interest" requires some consideration for the other fellow, for the other nation, for the other point of view; some giving with the taking. This applies with particular force to relations between man and the rest of nature.

The trend of human modification of the biological community is toward simplification. The object of agriculture is to grow pure stands of crops, single species of plants that can be eaten directly by man; or single crops that provide food for animals that can be eaten. The shorter the food chain, the more efficient the conversion of solar energy into human food. The logical end result of this process, sometimes foreseen by science fiction writers, would be the removal of all competing forms of life—with the planet left inhabited by man alone, growing his food in the form of algal soup cultivated in vast tanks. Perhaps ultimately the algae could be dispensed with, and there would be only man, living through chemical manipulations.

Efficient, perhaps; dismal, certainly; and also dangerous. A general principle is gradually emerging from ecological study to the effect that the more complex the biological community, the more stable. The intricate checks and balances among the different populations in a forest or sea look inefficient and hampering from the point of view of any particular population, but they insure the stability and continuity of the system as a whole and thus, however indirectly, contribute to the survival of particular populations.

Just as health in a nation is, in the long run, promoted by a diversified economy, so is the health of the biosphere promoted by a diversified ecology. The single crop system is always in precarious equilibrium. It is created by man and it has to be maintained by man, ever alert with chemicals and machinery, with no other protection against the hazards of some new development in the wounded natural system. It is man working against nature: an artificial system with the uncertainties of artifacts. Epidemic catastrophe becomes an ever present threat.

This is one of the dangers inherent in man's mad spree of population growth—he is being forced into an ever more arbitrary, more artificial, more precarious relation with the resources of the planet. The other great danger is related. With teeming numbers, an ever tighter system of control becomes necessary. Complex organization, totalitarian government, becomes inevitable; the individual man becomes a worker ant, a sterile robot. This surely is not our inevitable destiny.

I am not advocating a return to the neolithic. Obviously we have to have the most efficient systems possible for agriculture and resource use. But long run efficiency would seem to require certain compromises with nature—hedgerows and woodlots along with orchards and fields, the development of a variegated landscape, leaving some leeway for the checks and balances and diversity of the system of nature.

Ethical, esthetic and utilitarian reasons thus all support the attempt to conserve the diversity of nature. It is morally the right thing to do; it will provide, for future generations, a richer and more satisfying experience than would otherwise be possible; and it provides a much needed insurance against ecological catastrophe. "Unless one merely thinks man was intended to be an all-conquering and sterilizing power in the world," Charles Elton has remarked, "there must be some general basis for understanding what it is best to do. This means looking for some wise principle of coexistence between man and nature, even if it be a modified kind of man and a modified kind of nature. This is what I understand by *conservation*."

In defying nature, in destroying nature, in building an arrogantly selfish, man-centered, artificial world, I do not see how man can gain peace or freedom or joy. I have faith in man's future, faith in the possibilities latent in the human experiment: but it is faith in man as a part of nature, working with the forces that govern the forests and the seas; faith in man sharing life, not destroying it.

IX

THE BARREN, dusty lands at the eastern end of the Mediterranean Sea were once green and fruitful, the author of this selection reminds us. Civilizations rose and flourished there. Cities grew—and men cut down the trees for firewood and building materials. Men ravished the fertile valleys to grow food crops. Today, a few nomadic shepherds manage to wrest a poor living from the dusty hills and dry valleys. They share the land with archeologists who scrape out the dry shards and bones of the ancient peoples and marvel at the scope of change.

Here, then, in ancient history, lie the roots of the ecological crisis we face today. Man's role in changing the face of the earth began a long time ago. It merely proceeds faster today, thanks to technology. And there are no more green and lush frontiers to which man can flee.

Why have we taught history without making it clear to every elementary school student that man's misuse of natural resources has caused wars, migrations and the fall of great civilizations?

This is just one of many important questions that Walter G. Rosen asks—and attempts to answer—in the following selection.

The Environmental Crisis: Through a Glass Darkly

"The Environmental Crisis: Through a Glass Darkly" by Walter G. Rosen is a corrected edition of the original article which appeared in *BioScience*, Vol. 20 (November 15, 1970), pp. 1209-1216. Reprinted from the corrected edition by permission of the author and the American Institute of Biological Sciences.

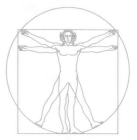

WE SOLVE our acute shortage of fossil fuels by turning to nuclear power and thereby create thermal pollution and a staggering radioactive waste problem.

We reprocess waste reactor fuel and thereby pollute air, water, and soil.

We find substitutes for our rapidly disappearing forests and thereby create non-biodegradable wastes. We dispose of the wastes by land-fill and thereby destroy wildlife habitats or by incineration and thereby pollute the air.

We place scrubbers in the incinerators and thereby save the air but pollute the water.

We create, by breeding programs, new high-yielding cereal crops (the so-called "Green Revolution") to alleviate the food shortage and thereby generate vastly greater fertilizer needs.

I could go on but the point should have been made by now. The problem is somewhere else. No amount of technological tinkering is likely to get at the root causes of the crisis. Indeed, it is probably safe to say that thus far every apparent solution to an environmental problem has generated one or more problems as serious as the problem it was designed to cure.

Why has the Western world, the industrialized world, the portion of the world with the highest literacy and the greatest scientific and technological sophistication blundered into this crisis? I am not enough of a historian, social psychologist, economist, political scientist, anthropologist, or philosopher to answer that question adequately. I do know, though, that the answer is not to be found in a simplistic castigation of capitalism. The Western (and Eastern) industrialized world includes the socialist countries as well as the capitalist. What both seem to share is the growth gestalt: the "cowboy" or "frontier" or "flat earth" world view as opposed to the "spaceship" or "finite system" or "round earth" world view.

The latter view is derived from the totally new fact that we have run out of frontiers, run out of space, and run out of resources. It is based on the fact that, suddenly, there are too many of us. It is based, further, on the shocking realization that our environment does not provide us with diluents, either gaseous or aqueous, of infinite volume.

Even were the volume infinite we now know that some noxious substances simply do not dilute but rather are concentrated as they move through food webs. Still worse news if one thinks of our planet as the balanced biosphere which it is (or was): the DDT in the ocean, even before it enters food chains, is present in quantities sufficient to impair the photosynthetic efficiency of the marine phytoplankton on which the entire aquatic food pyramid is dependent.[1]

The ultimate problem, of course, is too many people. I will not bore the reader with a repetition of facts and figures which by now have become familiar to all. Suffice it to say that the best estimates of optimal world population are less than 1 billion, that we have at present 3.5 times that number, and that total world population will double again in 30 years. And, of course, we all know that the high material standard of living which we enjoy generates ever-increasing per capita consumption of the fruits of our technological genius.

It has been estimated that in terms of damage to the environment (garbage production, consumption of energy, and of nonrenewable resources; removal of land from primary productivity, etc.) each American can be thought of as being the equivalent of 25 to 250 Indians, i.e., each of us does as much damage to the environment as that many of our "underdeveloped" brothers.[2] So proud are we of our standard of living that we want more of the same for our growing population and we export our values and thus generate similar appetites abroad. Our population is increasing at a "modest" 1.5% per year. Our power needs are increasing ten times that fast and we are already confronted with an urgent power crisis. Some countries are growing at 3-4% per year. Has anyone calculated the power needs which must be met if we are to gratify their "revolution of rising expectations"?

We are thus faced with the obvious necessity for a halt to the population explosion. More specifically, we are in urgent need of world-wide zero population growth; in some places, of negative population growth, and, equally important, of a re-examination of the wisdom of unfettered economic growth. This implies a redefinition of our concept of what constitutes a desirable standard, or style, of living.

Why have we blundered into such a serious situation? Where has our individual and collective intelligence failed us? Let me offer some tentative thoughts in an effort to diagnose our ills.

The Tinker's Assumption

It occurs to me that we have made the honest, thoughtless mistake of transposing from English common law a precious value when applied to *people* and made of it a pernicious precept by applying it to *things*: "innocent until proven guilty." It seemed, until recently, reasonable to apply this rule to "things," including synthetic molecules, combustion products, food additives, pesticides, medicines, packaging materials, highways, airplanes, explosives, dams, and rockets. By now we ought to have learned otherwise. The fission products of nuclear bomb testing should have taught us if radium did not. Thalidomide should have taught us, and DDT. But all of these experiences notwithstanding, we continue to assume that damage must be demonstrated before restraints are invoked. Thus 2,4,5 -T has been unequivocally demonstrated to be teratogenic and its use in Vietnam and in this country have been restricted. But as Thomas Whiteside pointed out in his recent book on defoliation 2,4,5 -T had never been tested for teratogenicity, or for any other form of human toxicity, before the first birth defects were reported from Vietnam.[3] And the present restrictions permit its continued use in this country while the case is appealed by the manufacturers. I visited a garden supply shop recently and found not only 2,4,5 -T for sale as a garden herbicide but also sodium arsenite, s-ethyl dipropylthiocarbamate, 7-oxabicyclo (2,2,1) heptane-2,3 dicarboxylic acid, 3,6 dichloro-o-anisic acid, and 2(2,4,5 -trichlorophenyoxyl) propionic acid in a variety of liquid and powder preparations for garden use. It seems reasonable to assume that these compounds are subject to the same restraints, or lack of them, as 2,4,5-T—innocent until proven guilty. And this is probably the case for most, if not all, compounds not intended for direct internal human consumption.

The application of the "innocent until proven guilty" concept to thermal pollution, defoliation, irrigation systems, high rise buildings, supersonic transports, etc., is too obvious to require elaboration. (The skeptical scrutiny to which continued funding of the SST is being subjected is a hopeful sign of change.) It is also too obviously wrong to require lengthy analysis. We have tinkered with the environment recklessly, with occasional dire results. We continue to tinker in a manner that invites disaster.

Tinker is a most inappropriate verb. We have intervened massively, to the extent of upsetting ecosystems, destroying species, altering the composition of the atmosphere, the depth of the topsoil, and the climate of vast regions of the earth. (Remember that the eastern Mediterranean was once a "Garden of Eden" and the Cedars of Lebanon were not fictional. Our role in changing the face of the earth has ancient historical roots. It is as old as our agriculture. However, thanks to machinery and new chemicals, the pace has increased vastly in recent years.)

What constitutes an appropriate amount of testing, and how to determine the degree to which we can or should attempt to anticipate the consequences of our actions is, of course, a major problem. One can reasonably argue the impossibility of anticipating the unanticipated. Perhaps this concern, with historical examples (e.g., from the work of Einstein to the devolopment of atomic weapons) belongs in the science curriculum. But this is a separate problem. The present difficulty is with our unwillingness and/or inability to alter present practices which are of already proven danger.

Why Do We Persist?

Why do we behave in this way? Why, in the light of overwhelming evidence that we are on a course of species suicide, do we continue our rape of the biosphere? Let me suggest some fragmentary answers.

First of all, I would contend that we have failed to teach objective truth as we have discovered it. As scientists and science teachers, we have been derelict in our duty. The fault is not entirely ours, since we ourselves have been the victims of a faulty system. Unwittingly, we have perpetuated as teachers the faulty science which was inflicted on us when we were students. I have developed this argument elsewhere[4] and will sketch it only briefly here.

Science as it is taught, from grade school through graduate school, is basically geared to the preprofessional. What we call science in liberal arts, or science for the nonscientist, is essentially a watered-down version of the encyclopedic view of science which we expect of the professional. Science taught in this way is probably badly conceived even for the future scientist, but that is another story. For now it is important only to note that, in spite of loud protestations to the contrary, we do not teach science as inquiry. We teach science as history: a collection of facts, figures, and terminology. We do not teach, for the most part, the skills of data collection, theory building, criticism, and interpretation. We do not teach the development of a critical faculty. We do not allow students (prior to graduate school, and often not even there) the thrill of discovery; we do not permit students to "fail intelligently."

Perhaps most importantly, we do not examine the sociology of science: the impact of science on humanistic and religious thought; the responsibility (or non-responsibility) of the scientist for the application of his discoveries; the relationship of science to government; "free" vs. "planned" science; pure science, applied science, technology. In short, we ignore, in the curriculum which claims to train scientists and in the curriculum which claims to make nonscientists at least moderately literate in matters scientific, the entire complex of questions which examine the relationship of science to society and culture. This includes, of course, the question of science teaching and research vis-a-vis the environmental crisis. The present discussion is admittedly quite general. The textual materials needed to come to grips with the specifics are, however, readily available. (There is a rich, varied, and rapidly growing literature, only an arbitrary sample of which can be mentioned here: the books of Dubos, Eisley and Bronowski; anthologies such as *The Subversive Science* [Shepard and McKinely, eds.], *The Mystery of Matter* [Louise Young, ed.] are certainly suitable for undergraduates and perhaps also for high school students.) The result of these sins of omission is that non-science students are for the most part merely bored and overburdened with an unmanageable hodge-podge of facts. At the same time they, along with future scientists, are denied access to insights and skills which would aid them in confronting the world in which they live as organisms, whether or not they wish to practice science.

Over 20 years ago Fairfield Osborn expressed a similar concern:[5]

It is extraordinary that with a few exceptions there is no such thing as the general teaching of conservation in our schools and colleges today. The study of history would be illuminated if emphasis were placed on the fact that conditions resulting from man's misuse of his natural resources were definite factors in the movements of peoples, and in the origins of wars. Likewise courses in economics, engineering, chemistry, biology, sociology and even philosophy would be vitalized if they included considerations of man's relationships to the natural physical world in which he lives.

Have we heeded this advice? Regrettably, we have not. And yet we have seen, in this country, considerable preoccupation with "modernizing" instruction, particularly in the sciences. What has been the result? Well, we recently saw the complete revision of the biology curriculum through the agency of the Biological Sciences Curriculum Study. The result was largely a set of new terminology to replace the old. Instead of memorizing the names of muscles and organs, our students now memorize terms like endoplasmic reticulum, mitochondrion, ATP, and the intermediates of the Krebs Cycle. In chemistry and physics they are learning the names of new subatomic particles.

But where do they learn about the chemistry of soil and air and water rather than test-tube reactions? Where do they learn about photosynthesis as an organismic or biotic process, rather than about the light and dark reactions, phosphoglyceric acid, and Calvin Cycle? Where do they learn about comparative reproductive physiology rather than the names of the stages of mitosis?

Show me the book, high school or college, that stresses the fact that all of the oxygen in the atmosphere is the product of photosynthesis, as is all fossil fuel. Indeed, where is a student to learn about biogeochemical cycles in a manner that makes meaningful the consequences of ecologically unsound farming, mining, and manufacturing?

Where is he to learn about primary productivity and trophic levels in a manner that relates to animal protein consumption and the U.S. standard of living? (There is an interesting parallel between our failure to teach science and our failure to teach other important social values. Think, for example, of how poorly most Americans perceive the basic instrument of our constitutional law, the Bill of Rights, despite the fact that courses in civics and history are required of all students in the grade and high schools. We teach terminology; the anatomy of government. We somehow fail to teach the meaning. Thus when the Bill of Rights was circulated as a petition in Ohio during the 1950s most people, of whatever background or walk of life, refused to sign it. A recent newspaper article reveals that this attitude continues. And numerous polls indicate that a substantial portion of the populace, often a majority, favors one or another legal measure which would amount to abrogation of a constitutionally protected right.) It is a pleasure to acknowledge that the "green version" of BSCS biology is a notable exception to this general indictment. I have the impression, however, that this is the least popular version, especially in urban areas where it is perhaps most urgently needed. College conservation courses often preach the gospel but quite evidently the message has not prevailed.

Thus, we have generally failed to teach science as inquiry, we have failed to teach meaningful relevance, and we university scientists have also failed to separate ourselves from our narrow research preoccupations in order to teach science as the mode of inquiry which permits us to perceive man *in* nature and *of* nature rather than manipulating nature.

We must learn this difference ourselves, and then we must teach it. Our survival is in danger. John Fisher has proposed that survival itself must become the pervading theme of education at the college level:[6]

. . . Let's call it Survival U. It will not be a multiversity, offering courses in every conceivable field. Its motto-emblazoned on a life jacket rampant will be: "What must we do to be saved?" If a course does not help to answer that question it will not be taught here . . . Neither will our professors be detached, dispassionate scholars. To get hired, each will have to demonstrate an emotional commitment to our cause. Moreover, he will be expected to be a moralist; for this generation of students, like no other in my lifetime, is hungering and thirsting after righteousness. What it wants is a moral system it can believe in—and that is what our University will try to provide. In every class it will preach the primordial ethic of survival.

If our survival is indeed in danger, we must act rapidly and radically. Not only in college but at every level from kindergarten through graduate school we must teach relevant science, ecological awareness, and the responsible kinds of behavior which follow therefrom. Charles Silberman has stated well, albeit in very general terms, the principles which underlie the kind of education I am trying to describe:[7]

To be practical, an education should prepare a man for work that doesn't yet exist and whose nature cannot even be imagined. This can be done only by teaching people how to learn, by giving them the kind of intellectual discipline that will enable them to apply man's accumulated wisdom to new problems as they arise, the kind of wisdom that will enable them to *recognize* new problems as they arise.

Education should prepare people not just to earn a living but to live a life: a creative, humane, and sensitive life. This means that the schools must provide a liberal, humanizing education. And the purpose of liberal education must be, and indeed always has been, to educate educators—to turn out men and women who are capable of educating their families, their friends, their communities, and most important, themselves.

According to William Arrowsmith, the chances for meaningful change are slight. Though he speaks specifically of graduate schools I suspect that his indictment applies equally well to all other levels of formal education:[8]

Our present system of graduate education is so much the creature of vested interests and dead tradition, contains so much sheer automatism, snobbery, and prejudice, and so little pertinence to the real needs of men, that any conceivably effective antidote would be too radical to be tolerated by its custodians and beneficiaries.

Arrowsmith's skepticism notwithstanding, we must act rapidly and radically for our survival is in danger. We must change not only our education system but our very life styles and our morality. We need a new code of ethics.

Some "New" Commandments

We hear talk of an "Ecological Bill of Rights." I submit that the very phrase reflects our mistaken perceptions. Rather than rights (freedoms for ourselves), we need a new set of "Thou Shalt Nots," an ecological Ten Commandments, with emphasis on restraints rather than freedoms.

The original ten commandments require little alteration to make of them a set of ecologically sound behavior precepts:

I am the Lord (radiant energy and the primary producers which transform it into chemical energy; clean water; mineral elements in limited supply; earth on which the green plants can grow; microorganisms which fix nitrogen, decompose complex organic matter, digest cellulose, stabilize soil). I have brought thee out of the land of Egypt, out of the house of bondage (the inorganic state; or, if you prefer, preconscious life).

Thou shalt have no other gods before me (the balance of natural ecosystems must be preserved; you shall not create a technology which shall upset the balance of natural systems).

Thou shalt not make unto thee any graven image (do not worship your machines; they cannot replace your limited stores of energy, materials and space).

Thou shalt now bow down before them and serve them; for I the Lord am a jealous god (if in your arrogance you build a high dam at Aswan, it will become silted up, and the fisheries beyond the delta will die for lack of the fertilizing silt; and schistosomiasis shall ravage the river valley).

Thou shalt not commit adultery (synthetic molecules, in food or medicine, can be dangerous traps; they can disrupt food chains; worse, they can lead to the conceits which will cause you to violate commandments two and three above. Fake foods and plastics are graven images if they come to rule your lives).

Clearly, the injunctions against killing, stealing, and covetousness are also ecologically sound precepts.

Now let me innovate a bit to be certain to include one of the most essential considerations:

Thou shalt stop at two children (be fruitful and multiply; but remember you are part of an intricate food web and if you deny other creatures their living space you are depleting My kingdom and upsetting the food webs on which you depend).

Now think about this. After the last commandment, in Exodus XX, Verse 25, the Lord says "And if thou wilt make me an altar of stone, thou shalt not build it of hewn stone; for if thou lift up thy tool upon it, thou hast polluted it."

Do I believe *that*? Literally? Well, not quite literally. I'm not a Luddite. I don't believe we should smash the machines or reject our technology. Rather, I believe that we must control it, and soon, for now it controls us, and it is destroying us. We must get off the back of nature, which we are breaking, and back into nature, of which we are a part. We must consume less and recycle more. We must begin with ourselves. We must struggle along without electric toothbrushes. We must not use the internal combusion engine (or any other engine, however less polluting, since their manufacture requires so much energy) when we can walk. We must live lower on the hog, which nutritionally means lower on the food pyramid. In a world short of food, burning protein for energy is perhaps immoral.

And so forth.

Can We? Yes. Will We?

Can we do it? Yes. We will need at least a 2-year moratorium on our professional activities as scientists while we restructure our educational system, revise our codes of personal behavior, suspend much of our gloriously entertaining and sophisticated research in molecular biology, theoretical chemistry, and physics and address ourselves to such urgent problems as rational land management, city planning, transportation, and reproduction control.

Will we do it? Probably no.

A few voices will cry out for drastic change. The rest of us will pretend to listen, make a few token gestures, and continue life essentially as usual. And for a very sound, perhaps uncontrollable biological reason. The change required of us is too great for us to contemplate seriously. The anxiety generated by confronting these obvious truths is too much to bear. We cannot give up so much that we cherish, however spuriously. We cannot change ourselves, to say nothing of changing others. And we cannot at the same time admit to ourselves that failing to change will bring our demise, if not as individuals then as a species. And so, in blind response to the stress-avoidance demands of our individual physiologies, we will turn off. (Psychologists refer to this phenomenon of stress-avoidance through subconscious distortion of major, unmanageable bad news into minor but manageable dimensions as "denial"—see Frank, Jerome. *Sanity and Survival.* Random House, 1967.) Not totally, of course. After all, here we are, changing detergents, yearning for lead-free gas, supporting planned parenthood, pretending to meet the crisis. But a moratorium on business as usual? Abandon our economy? Return to a less technological, less consuming, more nature-directed life style?

Hell no, we won't go! Because we can't bear the thought!

A colleague of mine, exhorting people to wake up to the approaching apocalypse, quotes Dylan Thomas exhorting his dying father not to give up life without a fight: "do not go gentle into that good night. . . ."

But I think he's wrong. We have to go gentle (or with a nuclear bang, but individually gentle). It's stress-reducing. It's the only way to keep our psyches from shattering. Or is there a way to face these awful truths, to act appropriately; to save the species and the rest of nature while we save our individual selves? Perhaps.

The total mobilization for World War II may provide a model. In that situation civilians willingly (for the most part) undertook a reduction in standard of living and academics applied their expertise to solving the pressing and immediate problems of modern warfare.

The threat to the environment and thus to the human species is certainly no less serious than that posed by the Axis powers and requires an equally profound and sustained response. But the threat is certainly more subtle and less clearly perceived. The duty of science education is to heighten perception and guide the response.

References

[1]Wurster, Charles F. DDT reduces photosynthesis by marine phytoplankton. *Science*, March 29, 1968.

[2]Davis, Wayne. Overpopulated America. *New Republic*, Jan. 10, 1970.

[3]Whiteside, Thomas. *Defoliation.* Ballantine. New York. 1970.

[4]Rosen, Walter G. Creative teaching and the biology curriculum. *BioScience*, 18: 1968.

[5]Osborn, Fairfield. *Our Plundered Planet.* Little-Brown. 1948.

[6]Fisher, John. Survival U: Prospectus for a really relevant university. *Harper's*, September, 1969.

[7]Silberman, Charles E. Murder in the schoolroom. I. How the public schools kill dreams and mutilate minds. *Atlantic*, June 1970.

[8]Arrowsmith, William. The shame of the graduate schools. *Harpers*, May 1966.

Ecology is—must be—vastly more than just one more branch of science, the author of this selection argues. The environment of man is social, political, economic and aesthetic, as well as biological and chemical; all attempts to analyze the environmental crisis and meet it with positive measures must cut across the rigid boundaries that have for too long separated the disciplines of learning. Today's need is for problem-focused programs of study in our educational institutions—because today's problems refuse to fit into the convenient pigeonholes of yesterday's curriculum.

In conclusion, the author states that for too long man has viewed his environment as an enemy to be conquered, or as a servant to be exploited. Can man change? Can he learn to respect his environment and to husband the precious resources that remain? This author casts his lot with those who answer, cautiously, "Maybe." He is without easy optimism, but not without hope.

Edward Kormondy's first field of study was zoology. He went on to specialize in limnology and oceanography, the twin branches of science that study the complex interrelationships of life in the seas and shorelands. Formerly a professor at the University of Michigan and at Oberlin College, Kormondy is now associated with the American Institute of Biological Sciences, the original publisher of this thought-provoking essay.

Ecology and the Environment of Man

"Ecology and the Environment of Man" by
Edward J. Kormondy is reprinted by permission
of the author and publisher from *BioScience*,
Vol. 20 (July 1, 1970), pp. 751-754. Published
by the American Institute of Biological Sciences.

UNLESS GROSSLY misperceived, I judge the
listening and reading audience of this symposium to be from among the washed. We
are of a kind and can handwring, hand-
shake, and back-pat with abandon. We
know how bad off the environment is, how
mismanaged our natural resources are, how
overpeopled, underfed and underwatered
the world is. We know how great ecology
is, how it has struggled to professional re-
spectability and national cognizance, how
influential it will be and thus why the col-
legiate everyman must be cleansed in the
waters of an ecology course. Alas, my
friends, we are here talking to ourselves—
we should be speaking from different plat-
forms and writing to different audiences.
Worse, we are looking through a glass darkly—ecology is not *the* answer, it is but a
fragmentary component of a complex system. We are striving against something
perhaps insoluble—not a man-generated
sociopolitical technology but man's very
ethic, his own view of himself in the world.
To these issues I shall direct my remarks.

The Speaker and the Audience

"Ecology" and "environment" are popular
and commonplace conversation pieces. It
is virtually impossible to scan any reading
material, except perhaps the girlie magazines, without encountering one of the
terms, or an equivalent. Even the PR-slicks
on the commercial airlines are in vogue:
Time, Life, Look, and *Sports Illustrated*
are doing it, and quite well, too. Learned
journals like *Daedalus*, sophisticated magazines like *Saturday Review*, scientific or-

gans like *Science* are in there pitching. But, what have you read lately in the pages of ecclesiastical ecological revelation, that is, in *Ecology, Ecological Monographs,* and *Limnology and Oceanography* on man's ecological relationship to his environment? on developments in undergraduate or graduate curriculums in ecology? on the place of ecology in the grade schools or in adult education? Not a (four-letter word) thing! In the argot of the day, ecologists "do their thing" in ecology and in *Ecology.* Where is the forum? Not in the official party organ, rather in some very well-heeled orphans!

As an index to the noise level in the forum, we can refer to a bibliography on "Science and Society" being prepared by the AAAS Commission on Science Education and dealing with the use of scientific knowledge for the benefit of man. Scanning some 100,000 pages to compile the entire list, the editor, John Moore, has identified about 500 titles which deal with such ecological territories as population, food and nutrition, pollution, and natural resources. Considering that most of these titles were published in the period 1960-69, and largely in *Science* and *Scientific American*, it is evident that our prodigious community has been prolific indeed.

But, the concerned elite have been writing to themselves profusely as if enjoying this self-flagellation. By numbers alone, the topic must surely be effete for intellectuals. The average Mr. American, whose reading level I am told is equivalent to 10th grade, is not reading these prestigious journals. He may look at the pictures in the slick magazines, but actually, he does not read much at all; yet he pulls the voting booth lever, some 50 million times in the past presidential election. How many ecologists, especially those who claim the centrality of ecology to man's environmental mess, are pumping stuff into such magazines?

If Mr. Average American does not read, what does he do? He is stuck to the boob tube an average of 3 hours an evening, much more on the weekend. And, how many TV shows have there been on the ecological crises? Precious few, and the best have been on the education networks which Mr. Average does not watch at all. Where were the ecologists in those shows? What are they doing about future shows? Precious little. Where are the ecologists? Largely in the field and the lab "doing their thing" and at the typewriter writing about it for the professional journals.

On yet another tack, where have the professional ecologists been in the conservation movement? A few here and there, but the major conservation/preservation organizations have been largely lacking the kind of ecological expertise which would have rendered to them a much-needed competence and sophistication and, in consequence, a much more powerful and influential lobby. Instead, the ecologists largely pooh-poohed the "little old ladies in tennis shoes" as early morning dickey-bird watchers instead of providing some understanding of the ecological dynamo in which both the dickey bird and the little old lady interact. Critical observers of the conservation scene have long deplored the poor-cousin status afforded them by the professional ecologist; they also now acknowledge a pervading anxiety as the professionals move to "take over." This is a long-overdue courtship and marriage in which the ecologist has been the dilatory suitor; now the bride is becoming increasingly and quite understandably frigid.

Exaggeration, rabble rousing, inflammatory—I accept those slings and arrows of outrageous ecologists; unfounded, inconsiderate, unprofessional—I sling those arrows back. There is considerable truth here; there is a real dimension of concern, too. There is a calling for the ecologist to put himself forward, not to impress his colleagues (even if it helps) or his students, but to contribute to understanding by that boob-tube bumpkin, public at large.

That there is a forum of any kind is salutary; that more heat than light is generated is deplorable, but understandable. The kind of ecology that my colleagues have described, the primary discipline-type ecology, is new; consequently, it does not yet have the comprehensive quality it aspires—its data cupboard is still pretty bare, its theory slots pretty few. Yet, some preeminent ecologists are carrying the torch of ecological concern nationwide, while the fuel source of broad-based basic information at the end of the torch, in spite of IBP (International Biological Program), is replenished much too slowly. With due apologies to Edna St. Vincent Millay . . .

But, oh, my foes, and oh, my friends—
Ecology may not last the night.

At this juncture, it should become apparent that I do not intend to spend time describing man as an integer of nature, and hence like all organisms both a creator and modifier of environment. This is axiomatic for our tribe, it does not need elaboration for the hearer or reader, most of whom are also of the tribe or are clamoring to join up —the wampum is attractive right now, the bandwagon loud and clear. Whatever I could say would be repetitious; it has been said better, more fully, more dramatically in many of the 500 papers John Moore has cited. Instead, I want to continue to speak to the title of this essay in ways not anticipated by the symposium progenitors.

Ecology as a Less Than Half-Truth in the Environment of Man

The "and" in the title given me, "Ecology and the Environment of Man," is particularly portentous of what I want to say. Grammatically, "and" is a conjunction, a connecting word, conjoining in this case two separate pieces. The environment of man is multidimensional, multidirectional, multifactorial; it is social, political, economic, aesthetic, and more as well as physical, chemical, and biological. It yields to analysis and understanding through no single view, no single discipline. The ecologist is but part of this insight-achieving into man's environment, it provides but a fraction of the "truth."

I want to develop this point more, because it is the crux of the theme; but before doing so, I need to remind you that pristine ecology is a Johnny-come-latter-day zealot in the race for leadership in resolving environmental crisis. If you doubt this, look at all but the very recent textbooks in both introductory biology and ecology. The environment-of-man kind of topic, if it appears at all, does so as a kind of conscience assuager, an afterthought at the end of the book and is *dubbed* "applied ecology" or "human ecology." Such sections are usually unexcitedly written; nor do they have any seemingly true awareness of "man in nature." Although conservationists (like Aldo Leopold and Joseph Wood Krutch) and reputable ecologists (like Marston Bates, especially in his *Where Winter Never*

Comes) called, few heard. Maybe it was the distaff's *Silent Spring* that did it. I will not try to pinpoint it, but the evidence is there for those who need convincing that the ecologist has arrived late on the environmental crises scene. Pure ecology liked to see those quadrat counts and frequency indexes, those life histories and gut analyses, those productivity measurements and migration records—not the real ecological problems. Somewhere along the line someone yelled. "Hey, fellas, come on in."

And, ecologists, it seems to me, have tried since to buy all available tickets to effect a de facto disciplinary segregation saying, in effect, that ecology will handle it from here out. It cannot be so. The environment is not just ecological!

Singling out and firing at the ecologist this way does some injustice; his colleagues in anthropology and sociology, in chemistry and physics, in literature and the arts are not above reproach, their precious professionalism not inviolate. The ivory tower of academic isolation from the nitty-gritty of every day, from "where it's at," has come home to roost, to haunt and taunt. This purist, or if you will, asocial spirit will be exorcized, but only by discipline pride-swallowing and interdisciplinary ablutions, by an integrated, comprehensive approach the likes of which are now beginning to emerge, or perhaps explode.

Before discussing those new approaches, I need to make clearer the contention that ecology, in even its broadest definition as a branch of science, provides less than a half-truth in comprehending man's environment. To do so, I will focus briefly on three timely topics: the Commons, Cayuga, and the Courts.

THE COMMONS

Quite obviously, the reference is to one of the more provocative essays which has appeared recently in the science-society interface, Garrett Hardin's "The tragedy of the commons" (1968). Ecologist Hardin, one of the very few professional ecologist missionaries of the environmental crisis, applied the social institution known as the commons to man's environment with especial reference to space, air, and water. The "commons," of course, refers to the legal sanction which recognized that there are components of man's environment which have not been nor ever could be exclusively appropriated to any one person nor to any group of individuals; this is what is set aside for public use. The tragedy, the "solemnity of the remorseless working of things" (Whitehead, as quoted by Hardin), refers to the cumulative effect of individual self-interest which takes to itself more of the potential gain by taking more from the commons. If only the commons were infinite, there would be no tragedy; since it is, as Hardin notes, "Freedom [to exploit] in the commons brings ruin to all."

Because of this "remorseless working of things" in a finite universe, Hardin recognizes that the fundamental problems of environmental corruption are those for which there are no technological solutions, a view which is increasingly and widely recognized in scientific circles. He concludes that the resolution of this technological void is to be made in the political and social realm. Alas, there is in that kingdom also an increasingly and widely recognized view that there are no current political solutions to these same problems (Crowe, 1969)!

Hardin proposes a kind of administrative

solution, based on assumptions which, as Crowe points out, are, in turn, based on social myths eroding swiftly and remorselessly in contemporary society. As interim contributions, Crowe suggests that science can (1) "concentrate more of its attention on the development of technological responses which at once alleviate those problems and reward those people who no longer desecrate the commons," and (2) "by using the widely proposed environmental monitoring systems, use them in such a way as to sustain a high level of 'symbolic disassurance' among the holders of generalized interests in the commons—thus sustaining their political interest to a point where they would provide a constituency for the administrator other than those bent on denuding the commons."

Although I remain to be convinced that Crowe's substitute proposals to the scientific community are either feasible or judicious, I do subscribe to his contention that no sustaining contribution toward,

maintaining a habitable environment will be made by science unless there is a significant break in the insularity of the two scientific tribes. . . . This will not be accomplished so long as the social sciences continue to defer the most critical problems that face mankind to future technical advances, while the natural sciences continue to defer those same problems which are about to overwhelm all mankind to false expectations in the political realm.

Here, then, is one potent, but epistemologically oriented example of the less than half-truth that ecology provides: if natural science as a whole can provide only partial resolution, ecology perforce is circumscribed to play even a smaller part in the tragicomic human drama.

It is perhaps more than editorial coincidence that the admonitions of Crowe appeared in the same issue of *Science* that carried a call by John Platt to a large-scale mobilization of scientists of both tribes to solve our crises problems (Platt, 1969). To explore Platt's rationale as well as specific proposals for a pre-empting of basic research by a devotion to the application of designs developed by interdisciplinary research teams would require a symposium in itself. Platt's basic message is abundantly clear: the ecologist carries but part of the truth.

CAYUGA

Not "far above Cayuga's waters," but directly on her shores was to arise in the next few years a nuclear-powered electrical generating facility: at the moment it appears it may not. Why? Because the consciousness of a significant segment of those in the Cayuga environs was invaded and their conscience piqued—not alone the ecologists and other biologists of Cornell University, one of the truly distinguished centers of environmental biology, but also a substantial number of other academicians and, significantly, a number of lay persons banded as a Citizens Committee to Save Cayuga Lake. Their counter to community "progress" afforded by the traditional benefits of increased payrolls, a broadened tax base, and, to be sure, more residents, has been some hardhitting statements on the precisely unknown but assuredly inexorable untoward long-range effects on the lake of thermal pollution and on the recognized hazards occasioned by radioactive waste discharges, and particularly because the proposed facility would be the first not located in a flushing situation such as is afforded by a bay or river (not that the latter afford any real consolation).

What is, to me, symbolic in this instance is not the factual evidence nor the predictions and speculations—this is the basic stuff which limnology and ecology exude and/or excrete. The prized jewel here is not the confrontation itself; fortunately, we have had our concerned and crusading individuals and groups, a Joel Hedgpeth versus the utilities in the case of Bodega Head, or a Sierra Club versus the lumber barons in the case of redwoods. The pearl is the awareness on the part of a concerned and diverse citizenry that (1) our environmental actions have ramifications into the unknown, and (2) a series of skirmishes and battles are to be much less preferred than being in and part of the action from its inception. This is a concept of a true total community, a phenomenon which is developing elsewhere, slowly, surely. In some measure, it is parallel to John Platt's call for mobilization of social and natural scientists, but goes well beyond to include the practicalities of every day and of every man. The ecologist? Here, again, he has not but a fraction of the truth to offer.

THE COURTS

The final component of this trilogy is, hierarchically, yet a further extension of the fusion of scientist with scientist and of scientists with the community at large. It is a fusion of community and the courts, not alone those berobed dispensers of justice, but beyond to the grand dukes of governmental regulative agencies. For the audience, I need not detail the course that led just recently to the sanctions on DDT by Health, Education, and Welfare Secretary Finch, by governors and mayors. I do need

to acknowledge the crusading effectiveness of the Ralph Nader for Man's Environment, the Environmental Defense Fund (EDF), which recognized that the only effective leverage exists in the nation's courts. Were it not for these court actions, I wonder how long a wait we would have had for the federal prohibitions? The ecologists, of course, were commendably crucial not only to EDF's financial survival but to its expertise. But without the friend-in-court and without the court? No, ecology has less than half the truth.

The Curriculum—A Soluble!

In developing this perspective on the place of ecology in the contemporary ecological crises, I have not deprecated ecology per se. It is, as my co-participants here have indicated, a discipline in its own right, making effective and substantial contributions to an understanding of relationships of organisms and environment. Rather, I have maligned the self-image which appears to be developing among many ecologists as environmental saviors. Admittedly, we must have an environmental salvation if man is to enjoy some richness and quality in his environment, but the resuscitation will be only by collective collaborative effort. At the curricular level, this means disrobing the vested interests of departments and the disciplines they espouse and building bridges on the archipelago of humanists, social scientists, and natural scientists; by focusing on the problems of profound significance to survival and well-being; and by eradicating the notion that action programs are hostile to academic life.

Refreshingly, things are moving, even in conservative, tradition-bound academia. In 1958, the Natural Resources Study Committee of the Conservation Foundation held a Conference on Resources Training in Berkeley; to the conference were invited institutions developing multidisciplinary programs focused on the environment. Only 20 were so identified! In 1969, the number was an order of magnitude greater, according to a survey conducted by Maria Grimes and supervised by Richard Carpenter of the Environmental Policy Division, Legislative Reference Service, Library of Congress, at the request of Congressman Emilio Q. Daddario, Chairman of the Subcommittee on Science, Research and Development (1969). Of 2000 accredited colleges and universities surveyed on the question of whether a multidisciplinary unit of any kind had been created or was being planned to deal with the numerous and varied fields of environmental education and/or research, nearly 500 responded indicating something was going on. Of these, 121 were selected as having a pertinent and viable program in operation or on the drawing boards.

The common denominator of these centers of environmental sciences appears to be a nonuniformity of model: "No single structural pattern predominates." In his letter of transmittal to George P. Miller, Chairman of this Committee on Science and Astronautics, Congressman Daddario summed up this way: "The variety of approaches suggest no obvious answer exists to the mismatch of historical institutional organization and emerging social problems." The paradigm instead is one of diversity of nomenclature (from a conventional arctic studies to a provocative environmental arts and sciences), operational objectives in research and training (from basic pesticide research to air quality standards for a region), and origin (from a department of civil engineering to one on city planning). The uniformity which does obtain is that few involve the social sciences, virtually none includes the humanities although future plans include both components. There is in common, also, a general lack of innovation in administrative procedures and curricular programs, and a pervasive problem in funding along the traditional college and university budgetary lines.

Pertinent to the topic of this symposium, the report states, "While most centers concentrate on graduate and postgraduate instruction and research, efforts are underway to broaden their scope to include undergraduate work and nonscientific disciplines." And finally and deplorably, " . . . in only a few instances do the students have an official, active voice in decisions involving planning, curriculum, training, or research projects."

The questionnaires of the institutions with viable programs were subjected to detailed analysis by John Steinhart and Stacie Cherniak, who also held extensive discussions with faculty and/or administrators in multidisciplinary programs in more than 30 institutions and made detailed on-site visits to six universities (Office of Science and Technology, 1969). Their provocative report to the President's Environmental Quality Council sharpens the focus on the two features found to be essential to success for problem-focused programs:

1) Substantial or complete control of the faculty reward structure, and

2) Freedom to be innovative in introducing course material, educational programs, work study programs, and curriculum requirements for degrees.

There is an element of utopia in these prerequisites, denying as they do the perquisites of those bastions of academe, the department.

Although further discussion of the salient revelations contained in these two stimulating documents could be of profit, I wish merely to make the point that a multidisciplinary approach to an environmental problem-focused education in which ecology would play a significant role but perhaps not the lead is feasible and can be successful. A curriculum for the environment is soluble! It may necessitate phoenix-like reconstructions, but it is soluble.

The Prime Cause—an Insoluble?

I wish I could end on this upbeat. I cannot, for I am deeply troubled as to whether Man can solve the most fundamental of fundamental problems—his perception of nature and of himself. As Eastern Man struggles with an ethical concept that grants dignity to self and to all men, Western Man continues to be largely contained by Judeo-Christian tradition which constitutes "the historical roots of our ecological crisis" (White, 1967). Imbued with a perception of nature in which air, land, and water are exploitable because they are assumed to have been created to serve his purpose, the resulting ethic of resource husbandry of Western Man will, without question, lead inexorably to his downfall.

Twenty years ago, Aldo Leopold called for a rethinking about Man's relation to his environment, for a new ethic for the land (Leopold, 1949). Can Man achieve such a new ethic? Can he come to see that the environment is no longer an adversary to be conquered, a servant to be exploited, a property of rightful and eminent domain, a possession of unlimited capacity? Can he reorder and subsume his divined status into that of a natural and integral part of this earthly spaceship? So long as Man continues to conquer and exploit others of his own kind, what confidence can one have that his environmental ways will change, that a new ethic for the land will develop? Not much. Man's relationship to man and to environment may indeed be insoluble. Doth therein lie the solution?

References

American Association for the Advancement of Science, Committee on Science Education. *Science and Society*, a bibliography, John A. Moore (ed.). In preparation.

Hardin, G. 1968. The tragedy of the commons. *Science, 162*: 1243-1248.

Crowe, B. L. 1969. The tragedy of the commons revisited. *Science, 166*: 1103-1107.

Leopold, A. 1949. The land ethic. In: *A Sand County Almanac*. Oxford University Press, New York.

Office of Science and Technology, Executive Office of the President, 1969. The universities and environmental quality—commitment to problem focused education. A report to the President's Environmental Quality Control Council, by John S. Steinhart and Stacie Cherniak, Washington, D.C.: U.S. Government Printing Office.

Platt, J. 1969. What we must do? *Science, 166*: 1115-1121.

United States Congress. House of Representatives. Subcommittee on Science, Research and Development. Environmental Sciences Centers at Institutes of Higher Education. A survey of the 91st Congress, 1st Session. Washington, D.C. U.S. Government Printing Office.

Communities of living things, like individuals, grow, mature and eventually die, either from natural causes or accidents.

The mobility of animal communities prevents observation of this sequence. The plant community, however, offers an unusual opportunity to study community growth and development.

In the following article, Frederic E. Clements describes the complex evolution of plant communities in which man is a vital factor.

The Nature and Role of Plant Succession

From Frederic E. Clements, "The Nature and Role of Plant Succession," *News Service Bulletin*, Vol. 3, No. 30 (1935), pp. 241-245. Reprinted by permission of the Estate of Edith S. Clements.

DARWIN ONCE said that every traveler should be a botanist, since plants furnish the chief embellishment of all landscapes. Today it may be asserted with equal warrant that the traveler should be an ecologist if he is to understand the changes wrought by nature and by man upon the countenance of Mother Earth.

Even the everlasting hills are not ageless, for they are worn down by wind and water; lakes are filled, rivers grow old, and swamps become dry land subject to the plow. Intimately connected with these changes, hastening or retarding them and in turn being modified by them, are the populations of living things, interacting in a maze of causes and effects to render the mantle of life a veritable kaleidoscope.

Most responsive of these is the plant cover, forming the pattern of a complex community in which animals and primitive man in particular find shelter and homes and from which they draw food and materials. Every such community is essentially an organism, of a higher order than an individual geranium, robin, or chimpanzee, but possessing structure and development, and a coordination of functions and parts similar in many respects. Like them, it is a unified mechanism in which the whole is greater than the sum of its parts and hence it constitutes a new kind of organic being with novel properties.

Communities arise, grow, mature, attain old age and die from natural causes or by accident. They regularly reproduce themselves after partial destruction by fire, lumbering, clearing, or other disturbance, regenerating new parts, not altogether unlike the process by which a lobster grows a new claw or a lizard a tail. The final or adult community is termed a climax, by reason of the fact that it is the highest type of social organism capable of growing in a particular climate, and its process of growth is known as succession, from the series of transient populations that pass across the scene.

The driving force behind succession is climate, operating directly or more often indirectly through soil or terrain. Like the individual plant, the community is acted upon by the environment and in turn reacts upon the latter, modifying such ruling factors as water, light and temperature. The associated animals are affected less immediately by these, but find their chief relations with plants as the source of food, materials and shelter. Man has modified or evaded physical conditions to a large degree, but even he is much controlled by differences of climate, soil, raw materials and food.

Plants Indicate Conditions

The significant outcome of these relations is that both species and communities serve as measures or indexes of conditions and hence are known to the ecologist as indicators. In connection with land classification, agriculture, forestry, grazing, erosion, flooding, and water supplies, the use of indicators furnishes a method of primary importance.

They indicate not merely the present features of climate and soil, but they also possess the clairvoyance of forecasting future changes and the possibility of controlling them, as well as of deciphering past events. Thus, climax and succession have not only great practical applications, but also provide the open sesame by which

traveller or nature-lover may unlock the pages of nature's book and read the past and present of every landscape, and likewise its further story.

The primary indications have to do with climate and soil and the outstanding changes of the past, but woven into this pattern is the infinite variety wrought by man, directly through fire, settlement, logging, cultivation and so forth, or indirectly by grazing, erosion, flooding, draining. Each of these processes has its own indicator communities, and its major effects can be read with almost as much certainty as though recorded on the spot by an eye-witness. [Lately, the effect of atomic radiation on plants and animals demands serious attention—Ed.]

The Great Plant Climaxes

Everyone is familiar in a general way with the great climaxes of our country and especially with the two most extensive, the eastern forest of beech, maple, chestnut and oaks, and the prairies of many kinds of grasses. In addition to these are the great transcontinental forest of spruce and fir to the northward and the Barren Grounds of sedge and lichen stretching along the Arctic Circle from ocean to ocean.

Related to these and hence of single interest as seeming far out of place are the alpine tundras of Mount Katahdin, Mount Washington, and of Pikes Peak, Mount Whitney, Mount Rainier, and other high summits of the Rocky Mountains, Sierra Nevada, and the Cascades, all survivals of a distant time of glacial advance when the arctic tundra moved far to the south.

Each of these great communities consists of certain dominants, a ruling class drawn usually from trees or grasses and best fitted to the climate concerned, and of various subordinate groups, among which the flowering herbs of woodland and prairie are the most conspicuous and familiar. Each climax is the product of its particular climate and hence the indicator of it, and thus serves as the point of departure for all the disturbances brought about by man and for all projects of utilization, restoration and rehabilitation under way or projected in the present national program.

Kinds of Succession

Examples of the growth of climaxes, of their childhood and adolescence are to be found everywhere within the corresponding climate. Most frequently seen are those due to disturbances caused by man, but others with a much longer lifespan occur in pond and lakelet, on rocky ridge and cliff, in sand dunes and bad lands, on the exfoliating domes of Yosemite and in the sinter and diatom basins of Yellowstone geysers.

Wherever an area is bare or is denuded by natural agencies or by man and his animals, development begins, progressing slowly or rapidly in accordance as the site is water, rock or actual soil, and passing through a series of communities to end finally in the climax proper to each climate.

Primary successions on granite may require a thousand years or more between the pioneering crustlike lichens and the climax forest of oak or pine, and hundreds of years to fill a lakelet to the point where meadow or woodland can flourish on the humus soil. By contrast, secondary successions following fire or cultivation may take no more than a half-century for the complete cycle, and an abandoned field in the prairie may be reclaimed by the grasses in a decade or two.

Succession in Water and on Rock

Probably the most familiar kind of succession is that found in standing water, with its communities of pond-lilies, cat-tails, bulrushes and sedges. The pioneer colony of this series is founded by submerged stoneworts, pondweeds, hornworts and the like in water up to about 20 feet.

As these grow and decay, the pond is gradually filled to the level at which floating plants can push in and take possession. These then rule as conquerors for a while, but likewise bring about their own downfall by shallowing the water so that bulrushes, cat-tails, wild rice and reed-grass can invade, usually in this order. The remains of these accumulate even more rapidly and in a few decades the pool may become a wet meadow covered with sedges, which in their turn yield to grasses and afterwards to shrubs, or in some cases to the latter directly.

When the ruling caste of woody plants is once established in a forest climate, trees of small demands and rapid growth overshadow the shrub stage, and later yield to the invading phalanx of climax trees of slower growth but greater permanence. In the prairie region, the succession terminates with a community of drouth-resisting grasses, since the rainfall is not sufficient to permit the development to continue.

On rocky ridges, mountain peaks, lava fields and boulders everywhere, the course of succession is quite different. By contrast with water plants, the chief task of the pioneers is to convert rock into soil and to increase the water rather than diminish it. In the miniature deserts of rock-surfaces only the humblest plants can thrive, such as lichens and mosses which are capable of enduring desiccation for months.

The first settlers are crustlike lichens, which etch the surface and slowly produce a thin layer of dust. After many years leafy species gradually invade and carry the task forward, yielding to mosses as a thin soil appears in crack and crevice. As the soil increases in depth, tiny saxifrages and other "rock-bearing" herbs enter, and these are followed after an interval by grasses. From this stage, the general course is the same as that in succession from water, inasmuch as grasses are followed by shrubs and these by trees in the case of a forest climate.

Succession in Soils

Succession on sand dunes takes place more rapidly and dramatically since soil of a sort is already present and the major problem is to fix the shifting sand and enrich it with plant remains. To be a sand binder, a plant must not only be well-anchored and hold sand, but it must also be able to catch the load borne by the wind and even more important, to keep its "head" above the sand as the latter heaps up about it.

The early invaders are lowly annuals of small requirements, which gradually stabilize small areas for the entrance of an ascending series of perennials, either herbs or grasses. In the prairies, grasses of progressively higher demands replace each other in forming a permanent cover, while in forest regions the grasses yield ultimately to shrubs and trees.

The reconstruction of the adult community is a simpler and still more rapid process where fire or clearing has destroyed the climax. The soil usually is neither removed nor impaired, and in the case of fire is often enriched by the minerals liberated.

Mosses and liverworts appear almost at once, and during the first full season a complete cover of annual herbs and grasses may be formed. Many perennials and shrubs survive the fire and their root sprouts soon appear in large number, gradually overtopping the herbs, reducing the light and taking the lion's share of the water in the soil.

The herbs are conquered by bushes and low shrubs; these are succeeded by taller shrubs, and trees then begin to straggle into the copses, or take more or less complete control by means of sprouts. After a few decades a young climax forest is again in possession.

A somewhat similar course is followed in cultivated fields that are allowed to "go back," the term itself indicating some popular appreciation of the process of succession. Annual weeds dominate for a few years, and the usual communities of perennials, grasses, and shrubs gain successively a short period of mastery, and return to forest or prairie often requiring but two or three decades.

Forces Concerned in Succession

Succession depends for its opportunity upon the production of bare or denuded areas, but the driving force back of it is climate, each succeeding community becoming less controlled by soil or terrain and more by climatic factors until the adult stage or climax is attained.

The actual growth of the community is regulated by certain processes or functions by means of which soil and climate produce their effects. The initial processes are aggregation and migration, by which individuals are brought together to form communities. These react upon the soil and then upon the local climate to render conditions at first more favorable to themselves and later to the invaders that are to replace them, the actual conquest being brought about by the outcome of the competition for water, light, and minerals especially.

Within each community there is likewise a certain amount of cooperation, as seen in the reaction that produces shade, increases the organic matter in the soil, minimizes the effect of wind, or augments the moisture of the air. The plants and animals of the community also exhibit many essential interactions, in some of which the mutual benefit is striking, as in the pollination of flowers by insects and hummingbirds. When man enters the situation, such relations become much more varied and important, especially in the hunting, pastoral, and purely agricultural stages of human society.

Succession of Races and Cultures

It is obvious that human communities are subject to the control of climate and soil—to what have often been called geographic influences. They exhibit aggregation and migration, reaction upon the environment and increasing control of it. Competition has been rife between and within them, and out of this has gradually emerged a new function, cooperation, first within the family and then spreading to larger and larger units under a slow but inevitable compulsion.

Succession has been less clearly perceived in human communities, though everywhere prevalent in prehistoric and ancient times, while modern rivalries disclose certain aspects of it. The first recorded succession is that of Chellean, Achulean, Mousterian, Solutrian and Magdalenian peoples in Europe, while the most complex has been the sequence of races in Mesopotamia, from Sumerian to Akkadian, Amorite, Babylonian, Assyrian, Chaldean,

Persian, Macedonian, Mongol, Tatar and Turk.

Better known to us is the series of invasions that have swept over England, involving Pict, Goidel, Brython, Roman, Angle and Saxon, Dane, and Norman. A similar succession on our own continent is illustrated by the Maya, Toltec, Aztec and Spaniard in Mexico, by various Pueblan cultures of the Southwest, and by the trapper, hunter, pioneer, homesteader, and urbanite in the Middle West.

Succession as a Tool

The applications of succession to human problems and natural industries are manifold. They are exemplified in all the disturbances wrought by man in the vegetation of the globe, as already suggested in the case of fire and clearing. Succession is invoked for its benefits in the rotation of crops, and it lies at the root of systems of forest management, and particularly of afforestation and reforestation. It is indispensable to land classification, and hence to regulated grazing and the utilization of the public domain. It is the chief tool in the control of run-off, erosion and floods, and the conservation of water supplies for irrigation and urban use, as in the maintenance of all surface natural resources, including game.

How varied is its service may be shown by the appeal to it in the litigation between Texas and Oklahoma over the location of boundary formed by the Red River in which millions of dollars in the Burkburnett oil field were involved. The decision of the United States Supreme Court in favor of Texas was based upon the evidence obtained from succession studies made possible by the researches of the Carnegie Institution of Washington.

THE ORIGIN OF CORN has been a mystery that has intrigued botanists for centuries. The plant was unknown in the Old World before 1492, while in the New World it became the basic food plant of the pre-Columbian culture and also of the majority of modern cultures, including our own. A wild form of corn has never been discovered, despite extensive searches throughout the hemisphere. How did wild corn differ from modern, cultivated corn? Where did it grow? How did it evolve under domestication?

These are some of the questions for which the authors of the following article sought answers as they conducted excavations of five caves in the Valley of Tehuacán in southern Mexico. The report of their findings is a fascinating chapter in the story of man's investigation of his past.

Domestication of Corn

THE PROBLEM of the origin of corn has intrigued botanists and other students of plants for more than four centuries. The plant was unknown in any part of the Old World before 1492, while in the New World it was the basic food plant of all pre-Columbian advanced cultures and civilizations, including the Inca of South America and the Maya and Aztec of Middle America.[1] Although these facts point strongly to its American origin, some writers have continued to argue eloquently for an Old World origin. A living wild form of corn has never been discovered, despite the extensive searches for it which have been carried on in various parts of the hemisphere. The absence of a wild form has been conducive to speculation—sometimes reaching the point of acrimonious debate—about its probable nature. There has, however, been general agreement that modern corn is unique among the major cereals in its grain-bearing inflorescence (the ear), which is completely enclosed in modified leaf sheaths (the husks), the plant being thus rendered incapable of dispersing its seeds. How, then, did wild corn, which to survive in nature must have had a means of dispersal, differ from modern cultivated corn? Where did it grow? How did it evolve under domestication? These are some of the questions that comprise the corn problem.

Close collaboration in recent years between archeologists and botanists has furnished at least partial answers to all of these questions, and has also contributed to solving the problem of the beginning of agriculture in America and the rise of prehistoric cultures and civilizations.

The first substantial contribution of archeology to the solution of the corn problem was the finding of prehistoric vegetal material in Bat Cave in New Mexico, excavated by Herbert Dick, then a graduate student in the Peabody Museum of Harvard University, in two expeditions, in 1948 and 1950. Accumulated trash, garbage, and excrement in this cave contained cobs and other parts of corn at all levels, and these cobs and parts showed a distinct evolutionary sequence from the lower to the upper levels.[2] At the bottom of the refuse, which was some 2 meters deep, Dick found tiny cobs, 2 to 3 centimeters long, which were dated by radiocarbon determinations of associated charcoal at about 3600 B.C. Anatomical studies of these cobs led to the conclusion that the early Bat Cave corn was both a popcorn (a type with small, hard kernels capable of exploding when exposed to heat) and a pod form (a type with kernels partly enclosed by floral bracts which botanists call glumes and the layman knows as chaff).[3]

Because the Bat Cave corn was both a popcorn and a pod corn, Mangelsdorf undertook to produce a genetic reconstruction of the ancestral form of corn by crossing pod corn and popcorn and backcrossing the hybrid repeatedly to popcorn. The final product of this breeding was a pod-popcorn bearing small kernels enclosed in glumes on ears arising from the upper joints of the stalks.[3] This reconstructed ancestral form had two means of dispersal: seeds borne on the fragile branches of the tassel and seeds on ears at high positions on the stalk which at maturity were not completely enclosed

by husks. The reconstructed ancestral form served another useful purpose in showing the archeologist approximately what to look for in seeking prehistoric wild corn.

Prehistoric Corn in Northern Mexico

A second important collection of prehistoric maize came from La Perra Cave in Tamaulipas in northeastern Mexico, excavated in 1949 by MacNeish, who was then associated with the National Museum of Canada. The specimens from this cave, like those from Bat Cave, showed a distinct evolutionary sequence from the lower to the higher levels of the accumulated refuse.[4] The earliest corn, dated 2500 B.C. by radiocarbon determination of associated wood and leaves, was identified as an early form of a still-existing race, Nal-Tel, which Wellhausen *et al.*, who have classified the present-day maize of Mexico, described as one of the four Ancient Indigenous races of Mexico.[5] These earliest cobs were somewhat larger than the earliest cobs from Bat Cave and so gave some support to the assumption that the two radiocarbon dates involved, 3600 and 2500 B.C., might be relatively if not absolutely correct.

While excavating La Perra Cave, which is located in eastern Tamaulipas, MacNeish also made some preliminary soundings in several caves in southwestern Tamaulipas which persuaded him that still earlier corn, perhaps even prehistoric wild corn, might be found in the lower levels of the refuse of these caves. Accordingly in 1954, with the assistance of David Kelley, then a graduate student in anthropology at Harvard, he excavated two caves, Romero's Cave and Valenzuela's Cave, in Inferniello Canyon. The earliest corn from these caves proved, disappointingly, to be not earlier than the

La Perra corn but slightly later, about 2200 B.C.[6] It was, however, of a race different from the La Perra corn and showed some resemblance to the Bat Cave corn.

Of even greater interest was the discovery in Romero's Cave of a few specimens of teosinte, the closest relative of corn. Well-preserved specimens of the fruits of this plant occurred in a level dated 1400 to 400 B.C. Fragments identified as teosinte occurred in feces in a level dated 1800 to 1400 B.C. Since teosinte has not been found growing in Tamaulipas in modern times, it may be assumed either that its range is more restricted today than it was several thousand years ago or that teosinte was planted with corn as a method of improving it, a practice reported by Lumholtz to be characteristic of certain Indians of the western part of Mexico.[7]

While the excavations in Tamaulipas were in progress, another series of excavations was being made in caves in the states of Chihuahua and Sonora in northwestern Mexico by Robert H. Lister of the University of Colorado. In one of these caves, Swallow Cave, Lister uncovered at the lowest levels several tiny cobs similar in shape and size to the Bat Cave cobs, though slightly larger. Since it seemed inadvisable to sacrifice these to obtain radiocarbon determinations, they have not been dated. However, the fact that they occurred at a considerable depth (about 2 meters below the surface) and in a preceramic context suggests a substantial age. These earliest Swallow Cave cobs were identified as prototypes of Chapalote, another of the Ancient Indigenous and still-existing races of corn of Mexico described by Wellhausen *et al.*[8, 5]

During this same period another impor-tant discovery was made when Barghoorn *et al.* identified as pollen grains of maize some fossil pollen isolated from a drill core taken at a depth of more than 70 meters below the present site of Mexico City.[9] This pollen was assigned to the last interglacial period now estimated by geologists to have occurred about 80,000 years ago. Since this period antedates the arrival of man on this continent, the pollen was thought to be that of a wild maize which once grew in the Valley of Mexico and has since become extinct. Other pollen, considered to be that of cultivated corn, occurred abundantly in the upper levels—above 6 meters. The earliest of these upper-level pollen grains are assigned to the later part of the post-glacial optimum and are therefore no earlier than the earliest corn from Tamaulipas or New Mexico. Although the criteria used in identifying the fossil pollen grains have been questioned,[10] more recent studies made by Barghoorn and his associates, using phase microscopy, have revealed features in which the pollen grains of corn and its relatives differ conspicuously and have confirmed the earlier identifications. There now seems to be no doubt that at least some of the fossil pollen grains were those of corn. Thus, this fossil pollen settles two important questions: it shows that corn is an American plant and that the ancestor of cultivated corn is corn and not one of corn's relatives, teosinte or *Tripsacum*.

On the basis of his excavations in Tamaulipas and the discovery of fossil corn pollen in the Valley of Mexico, MacNeish concluded that the evidence for the earliest domestication of maize and the beginnings of agriculture in America must be sought further south. A reconnaissance made in Honduras and Guatemala in 1958 yielded no results of promise. Excavations in 1959 of Santa Maria Cave in Chiapas in southern Mexico uncovered corn and other vegetal material, including pollen, but none older than that which had already been found further north. Turning northward again, MacNeish made a reconnaissance of sites in Oaxaca and Puebla which led to the conclusion that the Tehuacán Valley of southern Puebla and nothern Oaxaca might, because of its dry climate and ever-flowing springs, offer the most promising site so far discovered for seeking prehistoric wild corn and the beginning of agriculture. A preliminary sounding in 1960, in one of the numerous caves in the cliffs surrounding the Valley, uncovered cobs which were thought to be those of wild corn. Full-scale excavations conducted the following season confirmed this.

The physical features of the Valley of Tehuacán are described by MacNeish in another article which also describes the culture phases that have been recognized. At first glance this valley, with its semiarid climate and its predominantly xerophytic, drought-resisting vegetation, may not seem to be a suitable habitat for wild corn, and in earlier speculation about where wild corn might have grown we did not associate it with such plants as cacti and thorny leguminous shrubs.[1] Closer examination, however, suggests that the habitat furnished by this arid valley may, in fact, have been almost ideal for wild corn. The average annual rainfall at the center of the valley is low (approximately 500 millimeters a year) and becomes somewhat higher both south and north of the center. About 90 percent of the annual rain usually falls during the growing season, from April through October.

The other months are quite dry—in mid-winter the Valley is virtually a desert—and comprise a period during which the seeds of wild maize and other annual plants could have lain dormant, ready to sprout with the beginning of the summer rains and never in danger of germinating prematurely and then succumbing to the vicissitudes of winter. Thus, although the perennial vegetation of this valley, which year after year must survive the dry winter months, is necessarily xerophytic, the annual vegetation (and wild maize would have been an annual) need not be especially drought-resistant. Modern maize is not notable for its drought-resistance and probably its wild prototype was not either.

The corn uncovered by MacNeish and his associates in their excavations of the caves in Tehuacán Valley is, from several standpoints, the most interesting and significant prehistoric maize so far discovered. (i) It includes the oldest well-preserved cobs yet available for botanical analysis. (ii) The oldest cobs are probably those of wild maize. (iii) This maize appears to be the progenitor of two of the previously recognized Ancient Indigenous races of Mexico, Nal-Tel and Chapalote, of which prehistoric prototypes had already been found in La Perra and Swallow caves, respectively. (iv) The collections portray a well-defined evolutionary sequence.

Prehistoric Corn from Five Caves

Before considering the corn itself, we should say a word about the caves in which the remains of maize were uncovered. Five major caves which were excavated—Coxcatlan, Purron, San Marcos, Tecorral, and El Riego—yielded maize in archeological levels. The caves were situated in three or four different environments, which might have had considerable bearing upon the possibility of wild corn's growing nearby and which might have affected the practice of agriculture (see figure 1).

Coxcatlan Cave, first found in 1960, was one of the richest in vegetal remains. Excavations revealed 28 superimposed floors or occupational levels covering two long unbroken periods—from 10,000 to 2300 B.C. and from 900 B.C. to A.D. 1500. Fourteen of the upper floors, those from 5200 to 2300 B.C. and from 900 B.C. to A.D. 1500, contained well-preserved corn cobs. The cave, a long narrow rock shelter, is situated in the southeastern part of the Valley in one of the canyons flanking the Sierra Madre mountain range (figure 1). The shelter faces north and looks out on a broad alluvial plain covered with grasses, mesquite, other leguminous shrubs, and cacti. Supplementing the meager annual rainfall is some water drainage from the nearby mountain slopes and this would have made it possible for wild or cultivated corn to grow during the wet season. In other seasons of the year irrigation would have been necessary for corn culture.

A few miles south of Coxcatlan, in the same set of canyons, is Purron Cave. This is a somewhat smaller rock shelter but it contains a long continuous occupation (25 floors) from about 7000 B.C. to A.D. 500. It is archeologically much poorer than Coxcatlan and only the top 12 floors (from 2300 B.C. to A.D. 500) contained preserved remains of food plants.

El Riego Cave, situated in the north end of the Valley (figure 1) only a mile north of the modern town of Tehuacán, is a deep recess which contained an abundance of preserved specimens. Its five archeological zones, however, do not extend far back in time and were deposited between 200 B.C. and A.D. 1500. The cave is in the travertine face of a cliff and faces south. Under these cliffs and flowing out from them are the famous Tehuacán mineral springs, and the soils in front of the cave are fertile and well watered. Because of the fertile soils and the abundant water there is an oasis-like vege-

Figure 1 *The principal physical features of the Valley of Tehuacán, Mexico, and the approximate locations of the five caves in which remains of prehistoric corn were uncovered. The insert shows the locations of other archeological sites which have yielded evidence on the origin and evolution of corn.*

tation around the cave. This is an excellent area for agriculture and it may even have originally supported a vegetation too lush for wild corn to compete with.

The last two caves, San Marcos and Tecorral, occur in a steep canyon in the west side of the Valley (see figure 1). They are small shelters situated side by side, facing east. Tecorral contained three floors and only the top floor (about A.D. 1300) had a few corn cobs. San Marcos, however, was very different; although small, it yielded five superimposed floors with an abundance of preserved maize and other remains. The top four floors have been dated, by the carbon-14 method, at about 4400 B.C., 3300 B.C., 1100 B.C., and A.D. 300, respectively, while the earliest one is estimated to have been laid down about 5200 B.C. The shelters look out over broad alluvial terraces covered by grass and small thorny trees. Plants collected from this canyon bottom reveal a number of endemics—species not found elsewhere in the Valley. The surrounding travertine-covered canyon walls and hilltops, however, have a vegetation like that of the Sonoran Desert. The area receives water in the rainy season and much of it floods the lower terraces. All occupations found in the caves were from the rainy seasons. Agriculture would have been possible in the rainy season with or without irrigation. The alluvial terraces would have furnished an almost ideal habitat for wild corn.

In all, 23,607 specimens of maize were found in the five caves; 12,857 of these, or more than half, are whole or almost intact cobs. There are, in addition to the intact cobs, 3273 identified cob fragments and 3880 unidentified cob fragments. Among the remaining specimens are all parts of the corn plant: 28 roots, 513 pieces of stalks, 462 leaf sheaths, 293 leaves, 962 husks, 12 prophylls, 127 shanks, 384 tassel fragments, 47 husk systems, 6 midribs, and 600 kernels. There are also numerous quids, representing 64 chewed stalks and 99 chewed husks.

The prehistoric cobs from the five caves can be assigned to six major and five minor categories. The frequency polygons of figure 2 show graphically the time of the first appearance of a type of corn, the corresponding cultural periods, and the relative prominence (in terms of percentages) of the number of identified cobs for each of these categories. The polygons show patterns similar to those exhibited by artifacts, and for good reason—man's cultivars are artifacts as surely as are his weapon points or pottery. A brief description of the types of maize represented by these categories follows.

Prehistoric Wild Maize

The earliest cobs from the El Riego and Coxcatlan culture phase, dated 5200-3400 B.C., are regarded as being those of wild corn for six reasons. (i) They are remarkably uniform in size and other characteristics and in this respect resemble most wild species. (ii) The cobs have fragile rachises as do many wild grasses; these provide a means of dispersal which modern corn lacks. (iii) The glumes are relatively long in relation to other structures and must have partially enclosed the kernels as they do in other wild grasses. (iv) There are sites in the Valley, such as the alluvial terraces below San Marcos Cave, which are well adapted to the growth of annual grasses, including corn, and which the competing cacti and leguminous shrubs appear to

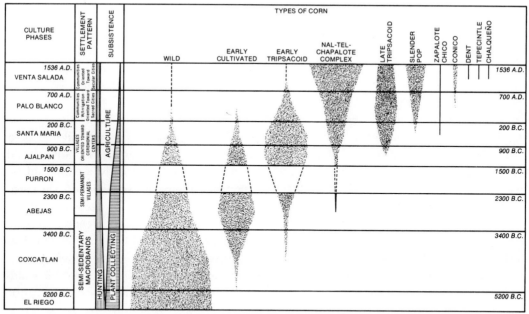

Figure 2 *Frequency polygons, in terms of percentages of number of cobs identified, showing changes in the types of corn in the Valley of Tehuacán from 5200 B.C. to A.D. 1536. Specimens of prehistoric corn were almost totally lacking for the Purron culture phase, which is recognized by other types of artifacts.*

shun. (v) There is no evidence from other plant species that agriculture had yet become well established in this valley, at least in the El Riego phase or the earlier part of the Coxcatlan phase. (vi) The predominating maize from the following phase, Abejas, in which agriculture definitely was well established, is larger and more variable than the earliest corn.

This combination of circumstances leads to the conclusion—an almost inescapable one—that the earliest prehistoric corn from the Tehuacán caves is wild corn. We shall assume here that it is.

The intact cobs of the wild corn vary in length from 19 to 25 millimeters (figure 3). The number of kernel rows is usually eight but a few cobs with four rows were found. None of the earliest cobs have kernels, but the number of kernels which they once bore

can be determined by counting the number of functional spikelets. These vary from 36 to 72 per cob. The average number of kernels borne by the earliest intact cobs of wild corn from San Marcos Cave was 55.

The glumes of the spikelets are relatively long in relation to other structures and are soft, fleshy, and glabrous (lacking in hairs). On some cobs the glumes are rumpled, probably as a result of the forcible removal of the kernels. The cobs have the general aspect of a weak form of pod corn.

The spikelets are uniformly paired and are attached to a slender, soft, and somewhat fragile stem (technically known as a rachis) in which the cupules, or depressions in the rachis, are shallow and almost glabrous, bearing only sparse, short hairs.

Most of the wild-type cobs were apparently once bisexual, bearing pistillate

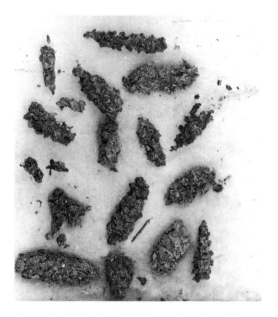

Figure 3 *(A) Cobs of wild corn from San Marcos Cave, representing the Coxcatlan culture phase, dated 5200 to 3400 B.C. These cobs are characterized by uniformity in size of the intact cobs, relatively long glumes, and fragile rachises.*

(female) spikelets in the lower regions and staminate (male) spikelets above. Of 15 apparently intact cobs from San Marcos Cave, ten had stumps at the tip where a staminate spike had presumably been broken off. In this respect the Tehuacán wild maize resembles corn's wild relative, *Tripsacum*, which regularly bears pistillate spikelets below and staminate spikelets above on the same inflorescences.

The uniformly paired spikelets and relatively soft tissues of the rachis and glumes provide further proof, in addition to that furnished by the fossil pollen of the Valley of Mexico, that the wild ancestor of cultivated corn was corn and not one of its relatives, teosinte or *Tripsacum*.

The wild maize declined somewhat in prominence in the Abejas phase, where it comprises 47 percent of the cobs. It per-

sisted, however, as a minor element of the corn complex until the middle of the Palo Blanco phase, dated at about A.D. 250.

What caused the wild corn finally to become extinct? We have for some years assumed that two principal factors may have been involved in the extinction of corn's ancestor. (i) The sites where wild corn grew in nature might well be among those chosen by man for his earliest cultivation. (ii) Wild corn growing in sites not appropriated for cultivation but hybridizing with cultivated corn, after the latter had lost some of its essential wild characteristics, would become less able to survive in the wild. Of these two causes of extinction the second may have been the more important. Corn is a wind-pollinated plant and its pollen can be carried many miles by the wind. It is virtually inevitable that any maize growing wild in the Valley would have hybridized at times with the cultivated maize in nearby fields, which was producing pollen in profusion. Repeated contamination of the wild corn by cultivated corn could eventually have genetically "swamped" the former out of existence.

There is now good archeological evidence in Tehuacán to suggest that both of these assumed causes of extinction were indeed operative. The alluvial terraces below San Marcos Cave, where wild corn may once have grown, now reveal the remains of a fairly elaborate system of irrigation, indicating that the natural habitat of wild corn was replaced by cultivated fields. Abundant evidence of hybridization between wild and cultivated corn is found in the prehistoric cobs.

We have classified 252 cobs as possible first-generation hybrids of wild corn with various cultivated types and 464 cobs as backcrosses of first-generation hybrids to the wild corn.

Is there a possibility that wild corn may still be found in some remote and inaccessible locality in Mexico or elsewhere? We suspect not. Whatever wild corn may have persisted until the 16th century was almost certainly rapidly extinguished after the arrival of the European colonists with their numerous types of grazing animals: horses, burros, cows, sheep, and—worst of all—the omnivorous and voracious goats. To all of these animals young corn plants are a palatable fodder, one that is to be preferred to almost any other grass.

Wild Corn Reconstructed

A well-preserved early cob, an intact husk system consisting of an inner and outer husk from the Abejas phase in the San Marcos Cave, and a piece of staminate spike from the Ajalpan phase of the same cave provide the materials for a reconstruction of the Tehuacán wild corn. This is shown in actual size in figure 4. An ear with only two husks was probably borne high on the stalk and its husks opened at maturity, permitting dispersal of the seeds. Other early specimens show that the plants lacked secondary stalks, technically known as tillers; the leaf sheaths were completely lacking in surface hairs; the kernels were somewhat rounded and were either brown or orange.

In its lack of tillers, its glabrous leaf sheaths, its rounded kernels, and the color of its pericarp, the Tehuacán wild corn differs quite distinctly from a third Ancient Indigenous race of Mexico, Palomero Toluqueño, described by Wellhausen et al.[5] This finding suggests that the latter may have stemmed from a different race of wild

Figure 4 *Artist's reconstruction of wild corn based on actual specimens of cobs, husks, a fragment bearing male spikelets, and kernels uncovered in the lower levels of San Marcos Cave. The husks probably enclosed the young ears completely but opened up at maturity, permitting dispersal of the seeds. The kernels were round, brown or orange, and partly enclosed by glumes.*

corn growing in another place. Fossil corn pollen from the Valley of Mexico suggests still a third locality where wild corn once occurred. It is becoming increasingly apparent that cultivated corn may have had multiple sites of origin, of which southern Mexico is only one, but the earliest one so far discovered.

The corn which we have called "early cultivated" is similar to the wild corn except in size (figure 5). It has the same long soft glumes and the same soft, somewhat fragile rachises. It is probably a direct descendant of the wild corn, slightly modified through growing in a better environment. Initially the better environment may have been nothing more than that produced by the removal, by man, of other vegetation competing with wild corn growing in its natural habitat. Later the corn was actually

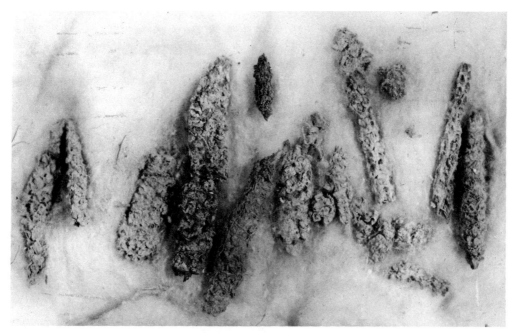

Figure 5 *Cobs of early cultivated corn from San Marcos Cave, representing the Abejas culture phase, dated 3400 to 2300 B.C. These are larger and more variable than the cobs of wild corn but are similar to them in having long glumes and fragile rachises.*

planted in fields chosen for the purpose. Still later it was irrigated.

Exactly when the maize was first cultivated in Tehuacán Valley is difficult to determine. Two cobs classified as early cultivated appeared in the Coxcatlan culture, dated 5200 to 3400 B.C., but we cannot tell whether the cobs represent the upper or lower part of this phase. Since remains of the bottle gourd and two species of squashes (*Cucurbita moschata* and *C. mixta*), as well as tepary beans, chili peppers, amaranths, avocados, and zapotes, occurred at this phase, there may have been at least an incipient agriculture and it is not unreasonable to suppose that maize, too, was being cultivated. However, two cobs scarcely furnish conclusive evidence on this point.

What we can be certain of is that during the Abejas phase, dated 3400 to 2300 B.C., this corn was definitely a part of an agricul-

tural complex which included, in addition to maize, the following cultivars: the bottle gourd, *Lagenaria siceraria*; two species of squashes, *Cucurbita moschata* and *C. mixta*; *Amaranthus* spp.; the tepary bean, *Phaseolus acutifolius*, and possibly also the common bean, *P. vulgaris*; Jack beans, *Canavalia enciformis*; chili peppers, *Capsicum frutescens*; avocados, *Persea americana*; and three varieties of zapotes. Among the 99 cobs representing this phase, 45 (almost half) were classified as early cultivated. Thereafter this type gradually decreased in relative frequency, becoming extinct before the beginning of the Venta Salada phase at A.D. 700.

Other Prehistoric Types

Making its first appearance in the Abejas phase but represented there by a single cob, and becoming well established in the Ajalpan phase, is a type which we have called "early tripsacoid" (figure 6). The term *tripsacoid* is one proposed by Anderson and Erickson to describe any combination of characteristics which might have been introduced into corn by hybridizing with its relatives, teosinte or *Tripsacum*.[11] In both of these species the tissues of the rachis and the lower glumes are highly indurated and the lower glumes are thickened and curved. Archeological cobs showing these characteristics are suspected of being the product of the hybridization of maize with one of its two relatives.

Since neither teosinte nor *Tripsacum* is known in Tehuacán Valley today and since neither is represented in the archeological vegetal remains, we suspect that the tripsacoid maize was introduced from some other region, possibly from the Balsas River basin in the adjoining state of Guerrero where both teosinte and *Tripsacum* are common today.

The introduced tripsacoid is a corn somewhat similar to the race (Nal-Tel) described by Wellhausen *et al.* but smaller.[5] This introduced corn evidently hybridized with both the wild and the early domesticated corn in the Tehuacán Valley to produce hybrids with characteristics intermediate

Figure 6. *Cob of early tripsacoid corn. This is characterized by stiff indurated glumes. It is thought to be the product of hybridization of corn with one of its relatives, teosinte or Tripsacum.*

between those of the parents. First-generation hybrids, in turn, back-crossed to both parents to produce great variability in both cultivated and wild populations (figures 7 and 8).

The introduced tripsacoid maize, together with its various hybrids, was the most common maize during the Ajalpan and Santa Maria phases from 1000 to 200 B.C. Thereafter it declined in frequency until it became almost extinct in the Venta Salada phase. But this complex apparently gave rise to two still-existing races of Mexico, Nal-Tel and Chapalote, and to a prehistoric type which we have called "late tripsacoid."

The earliest cobs from the Tehuacán caves were, because of their shape and glabrous cupules, thought to be prototypes of Chapalote, one of the Ancient Indigenous races described by Wellhausen *et al.* This race is today found only in northwestern Mexico in the states of Sinaloa and Sonora. Archeologically it is the predominating early corn in all sites excavated in northwestern Mexico and the southwestern United States.

Some of the later cobs from the caves, because their cupules were beset with hairs, a characteristic of the early Nal-Tel of La Perra Cave, seem to resemble this race more than they resemble Chapalote. Also, since Nal-Tel is found today in southern Mexico, it would not be surprising to find its origin there.

Actually Nal-Tel and Chapalote are quite similar in their characteristics, the principal conspicuous difference between them being in the color of the kernel, which in the former is orange and in the latter chocolate brown. Our hope that the first kernels to appear among the remains would enable us to

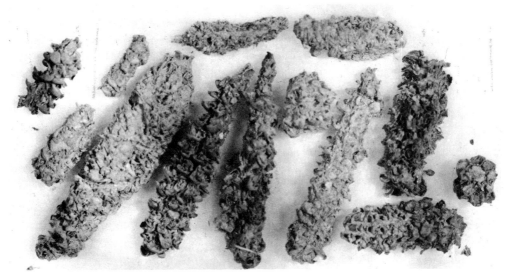

Figure 7.   *Various hybrid combinations resulting from the crossing of Tehuacán early cultivated corn with the early tripsacoid corn and backcrossing to both parents.*

Figure 8.   *Cobs from a single cache in San Marcos Cave, showing the great variation which followed the hybridization of the Tehuacán corn with the early tripsacoid corn. The two small upper cobs are wild-type segregates.*

distinguish between the two races was not realized. Of the kernels occurring in the Santa Maria phase, about half were brown and the other half orange, and both brown and orange kernels were also found in the later levels. Being unable, by any single criterion or combination of characters, to distinguish the cobs of the two races, we have designated this category the Nal-Tel-Chapalote complex (figure 9).

It was this corn, more than any other, which initiated the rapid expansion of agriculture that was accompanied by the development of, first, large villages and, later, secular cities, the practice of irrigation, and the establishment of a complex religion. If it is too much to say that this corn was responsible for these revolutionary developments, it can at least be said that they probably could not have occurred without it. Perhaps it is not surprising that present-day Mexican Indians have a certain reverence for these ancient races of corn, Nal-Tel and Chapalote, and continue to grow them although they now have more productive races at their command.

A type which we have designated "late tripsacoid" corn differs from the early tripsacoid primarily in size. It comprises principally the more tripsacoid cobs of the Nal-Tel-Chapalote type and were it not that it includes some tripsacoid cobs of a slender popcorn, it could be considered part of the Nal-Tel-Chapalote complex to which it is closely related and with which it is contemporaneous.

If the tripacoid cobs resembling Nal-Tel or Chapalote are considered along with these late tripsacoid cobs, this complex seems even more likely to have been the basic maize of the Tehuacán cultures from 900 B.C. to A.D. 1536, representing about 65 percent of all the corn at the end of the Venta Salada phase.

A type called "slender pop" has very slender cylindrical cobs, many rows of grain, and small rounded kernels, yellow or orange. This may be the prototype of a Mexican popcorn, Arrocillo Amarillo, one of the four Ancient Indigenous races described by Wellhausen et al.[5] This race, which is now mixed with many others, occurs in its most nearly pure form in the Mesa Central of Puebla at elevations of 1600 to 2000 meters, not far from the Tehuacán Valley and at similar altitudes.

Appearing first in the Santa Maria phase between 900 and 200 B.C., the slender pop increased rapidly and steadily in frequency, comprising 20 percent of the cobs in the final phase.

Judged by its cobs alone, the slender pop might be expected to be less productive than Nal-Tel or Chapalote, and its increased prominence deserves an explanation. A plausible one is that, although the ears are small, the stalks may have been prolific, normally bearing more than one ear. The present-day race to which it bears some resemblance and to which it may be related is prolific, usually producing two or three ears per stalk.

Minor categories include cobs and kernels which appear in later levels and which are recognized as belonging to several of the modern races of Mexico described by Wellhausen et al.[5] They occur much too infrequently to be of significance in the total picture of food production but they are important in showing that these modern Mexican races were already in existence in prehistoric times. The only previous evidence of this was the fact that casts of ears appear on Zapotec funerary urns.

Figure 9. *Cobs of the Nal-Tel-Chapalote complex from San Marcos Cave representing the Palo Blanco phase, dated A.D. 200 to 700. It was this corn, the product of hybridization between the Tehuacán corn and the early tripsacoid, which, in providing an adequate food supply, contributed to the rise of an advanced culture and civilization in Tehuacán Valley.*

Other Parts of the Corn Plant

In all, 3597 specimens of parts of the corn plant, other than cobs, were found in the five caves. These specimens confirm the conclusions reached from the study of the cobs. There has been no change in the basic botanical characteristics of the corn plant during domestication. Then, as now, corn was a monoecious annual bearing its male and female spikelets separately, the former predominating in the terminal inflorescences and the latter in the lateral inflorescences, which, as in modern corn, were enclosed in husks. Then, as now, the spikelets were borne in pairs; in the staminate spikelets one member of the pair was sessile, the other pediceled. The only real changes in more than 5000 years of evolution under domestication have been changes in the size of the parts and in productiveness.

The importance of these changes to the rise of the American cultures and civilizations would be difficult to overestimate. There is more foodstuff in a single grain of some modern varieties of corn than there was in an entire ear of the Tehuacán wild corn. A wild grass with tiny ears—a species scarcely more promising as a food plant than some of the weedy grasses of our gardens and lawns—has, through a combination of circumstances, many of them perhaps fortuitous, evolved into the most productive of the cereals, becoming the basic food plant not only of the pre-Columbian cultures and civilizations of this hemisphere but also of the majority of modern ones, including our own.

Summary

Remains of prehistoric corn, including all parts of the plant, have been uncovered from fire caves in the Valley of Tehuacán in southern Mexico. The earliest remains, dated 5200 to 3400 B.C., are almost certainly those of wild corn. Later remains include cultivated corn and reveal a distinct evolutionary sequence which gave rise ultimately to several still-existing Mexican races. Despite a spectacular increase in size and productiveness under domestication, which helped make corn the basic food plant of the pre-Columbian cultures and the civilizations of America, there has been no substantial change in 7000 years in the fundamental botanical characteristics of the corn plant.

References

[1] P. C. Mangelsdorf and R. G. Reeves, "The origin of Indian corn and its relatives," *Texas Agr. Expt. Sta. Bull. No. 574* (1939).

[2] _____ and C. E. Smith, Jr., in *Botanical Museum Leaflets, Harvard Univ.* 13, 213 (1949).

[3] P. C. Mangelsdorf, *Science* 128, 1313 (1958).

[4] _____ , R. S. MacNeish, W. C. Galinat, in *Botanical Museum Leaflets, Harvard Univ.* 17, 125 (1956).

[5] E. J. Wellhausen, L. M. Roberts, E. Hernandez, in collaboration with P. C. Mangelsdorf, *Races of Maize in Mexico* (Bussey Institution, Harvard University, Cambridge, Mass., 1952).

[6] R. S. MacNeish, *Trans. Am. Phil. Soc.* 48, pt. 6, 1 (1958).

[7] C. Lumholtz, *Unknown Mexico* (Scribner, New York, 1902).

[8] P. C. Mangelsdorf and R. H. Lister, in *Botanical Museum Leaflets, Harvard Univ.* 17, 151 (1956).

[9] E. S. Barghoorn, M. K. Wolfe, K. H. Clisby, in *Botanical Museum Leaflets, Harvard Univ.* 16, 229 (1954).

[10] E. B. Kurz, J. L. Liverman, H. Tucker, *Bull. Torrey Botan. Club* 87, 85 (1960).

[11] E. Anderson and R. O. Erickson, *Proc. Natl. Acad. Sci. U.S.* 27, 436 (1941).

XIII

MANY SCIENTISTS have looked to the study of animal behavior as a promising source for illuminating the complex relationships between man and his environment. Nikolaas Tinbergen has been particularly concerned with the mechanics of behavioral stimulus-response systems.

The following article, a portion of a chapter from his book, *The Study of Instinct*, presents some of the work that led him to conclude that instinctive behavior is dependent on both external and internal forces. He also offers a tentative definition of instinct—a term that has been the center of much controversy. He defines it as being a highly ordered nervous mechanism that may be primed, released and directed by both internal and external impulses; the animal's response occurs as coordinated movements that contribute to the maintenance of the individual and the species.

An Attempt at Synthesis

Recapitulation

We have now arrived at a point where it is necessary to review our results in order to evaluate and appreciate their significance in relation to our main problem, that is, the problem of the causation of instinctive behavior.

The foregoing chapters have led to the following conclusions.

Instinctive behavior is dependent on external and internal causal factors. The external factors, or sensory stimuli, are of a much simpler nature than our knowledge of the potential capacities of the sense organs would make us expect. Yet they are not so simple as the word 'stimulus' would suggest, for the 'sign stimuli' have gestalt character, that is to say, they release configurational receptive processes. The various sign stimuli required for the release of an instinctive activity co-operate according to the rule of heterogeneous summation. These facts led us to the postulation of Innate Releasing Mechanisms, one of which is possessed by each separate reaction. Apart from releasing stimuli, directing stimuli play a part, enabling or forcing the animal to orient itself in relation to the environment. The internal causal factors controlling, qualitatively and quantitatively, the motivation of the animal may be one of three kinds: hormones, internal sensory stimuli, and, perhaps, intrinsic or automatic nervous impulses generated by the central nervous system itself. Instinctive 'reactions' are of varying degrees of complexity; even the simplest type, the 'fixed pattern,' depends on a system of muscle contractions which is of a configurational character.

These results are incomplete in more than one respect. First, the evidence is still very fragmentary, and the generalizations are still of a very tentative nature. Second, the work done thus far has been mainly analytical, and no attempt has yet been made to combine the separate conclusions into a picture of the causal structure underlying instinctive behaviour as a whole. We have, however, gained one thing: we are realizing more and more clearly that the physiological mechanisms underlying instinctive behaviour are much more complicated than we were able to see at the start. Previous attempts at synthesis, such as Pavlov's reflex theory and Loeb's tropism theory, now appear to be grotesque simplifications.

While thus realizing both the relative paucity of analytical data and the complexity of the causal structure, we will nevertheless venture to sketch, in rough outline, a synthetic picture of the organization of the partial problems within the main problem as a whole.

Differences in Degree of Complexity of 'Reactions'

So far I have been using the terms 'reactions,' 'motor response,' 'behaviour pattern,' 'movement' for muscle contractions of very different degrees of complexity. This fact is of paramount importance, and I will emphasize it by presenting some more instances.

As we have seen, the swimming of an eel is a relatively simple movement. In every somite there is alternating contraction of the longitudinal muscles of the right and the left half of the trunk. In addition, the pendulum movements of successive somites are slightly out of step, each somite contracting a short time after its predecessor. The result is the propagation of the well-known sinusoid contraction waves along the body axis. (Gray, 1936.)

The swimming movements of a fish like Labrus or Sargus, as described by von Holst (1935, 1937), are more complex. The pectoral fins, moving back and forth in alternation, are also in step with the dorsal, caudal, and anal fins, each of which makes pendulum movements as well.

The movement of a male stickleback ventilating its eggs is of a similar type. The pectorals make pendulum movements alternately. This motion is directed forward, resulting in a water current from the fish to the nest. In order to counteract the backward push this exerts upon the fish, forward swimming movements of the tail are made in absolute synchronization with the rhythm of the pectorals.

Although locomotion might be considered merely an element of a 'reaction' in the sense in which I have been using this term, the stickleback's ventilating movement is a complete reaction, responding in part to a chemical stimulus emanating from the nest.

The reaction of a gallinaceous chick to a flying bird of prey is, again, somewhat more complicated. It may consist of merely crouching, but often it consists of running to shelter provided by the mother or by vegetation, crouching, and continuously watching the predator's movements.

Finally, a male stickleback in reproductive condition responds to visual and temperature stimuli of a rather simple type by behaviour of a very complicated pattern: it settles on a territory, fights other males, starts to build a nest, courts females, and so on.

Hierarchical Organization

A closer study of these differences in complexity leads us to the conclusion that the mechanisms underlying these reactions are arranged in a hierarchical system, in which we must distinguish between various levels of integration.

The reproductive behaviour of the male stickleback may be taken as an example.

In spring, the gradual increase in length of day brings the males into a condition of increased reproductive motivation, which drives them to migrate into shallow fresh water. Here, as we have seen, a rise in temperature, together with a visual stimulus situation received from a suitable territory, releases the reproductive pattern as a whole. The male settles on the territory, its erythrophores expand, it reacts to strangers by fighting, and starts to build a nest. Now, whereas both nest-building and fighting depend on activation of the reproductive drive as a whole, no observer can predict which one of the two patterns will be shown at any given moment. Fighting, for instance, has to be released by a specific stimulus, viz. 'red male intruding into the territory.' Building is not released by this stimulus situation but depends on other stimuli. Thus these two activities, though both depend on activation of the reproductive drive as a whole, are also dependent on additional (external) factors. The influence of these latter factors is, however, restricted, they act upon either fighting or building, not on the reproductive drive as a whole.

Now the stimulus situation 'red male in-truding,' while releasing the fighting drive, does not determine which one of the five types of fighting will be shown. This is determined by additional, still more specific stimuli. For instance, when the stranger bites, the owner of the territory will bite in return; when the stranger threatens, the owner will threaten back; when the stranger flees, the owner will chase it, and so on.

Thus the effect of a stimulus situation on the animal may be of different kinds. The visual stimulus 'suitable territory' activates both fighting and nest-building, the visual situation 'red male in territory' is specific in releasing fighting, but it merely causes a general readiness to fight and does not determine the type of fighting. Which one of the five motor responses belonging to the fighting pattern will be shown depends on sign stimuli that are still more restricted in effect. The tactile stimulus 'male biting' releases one type of fighting, the visual stimulus 'male threatening' releases another type. The stimulus situations are not of an essentially different order in all these cases, but the results are. They belong to different levels of integration and, moreover, they are organized in a hierarchical system, like the staff organization of an army or other human organization (figure 1). The facts (1) that at each of the levels an external stimulus can have a specific releasing influence and (2) that each reaction has its own motor pattern, mean that there is a hierarchical system of IRMs and of motor centres. So far as we can judge at present, each IRM is able to collect sensory impulses according to the rule of heterogeneous summation, and each motor centre controls a configurational pattern of muscle contractions.

The principle of hierarchical organization has been tested in but three cases: the

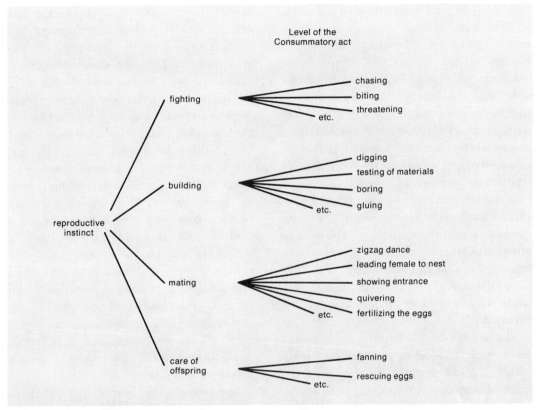

Level of the
Consummatory act

Figure 1 *The principle of hierarchical organization illustrated by the reproductive instinct of the male three-spined stickleback. (After Tinbergen, 1942.)*

digger wasp Ammophila campestris (Baerends, 1941), the three-spined stickleback (Tinbergen, 1942), and the turkey (Räber, 1948), and although the principle is undoubtedly sound, nearly nothing is shown in detail about the way it works out in the various drives and in different species of animals. Before a more detailed discussion can be attempted, a closer consideration of motor responses is necessary.

Appetitive Behaviour and Consummatory Act

The activation of a centre of the lowest level usually, perhaps always, results in a relatively simple motor response: biting, chasing, threatening, etc., in the case of fighting in the stickleback; actual eating, actual escape, actual coition, etc., in other instincts. This type of response has been the object of our analysis in most of the cases treated in the preceding chapters. This is no accident; it is the natural outcome of the tendency to analyse which leads to a conscious or (more often) unconscious selection of relatively simple and stereotyped phenomena.

These relatively simple responses are, usually, the end of a bout of prolonged activity, and their performance seems to 'satisfy' the animal, that is to say, to bring about a sudden drop of motivation. This means that such an end-response consumes the specific impulses responsible for its activation. Fighting, eating, mating, 'playing the broken wing,' etc., are, as a rule, 'self-exhausting.' Craig (1918), in a most remarkable paper that has not received the attention it deserves, was the first to single out these elements of behaviour; he called them 'consummatory actions.' Lorenz (1937), realizing that they constitute the most characteristic components of instinctive behaviour, that is to say those components that can be most easily recognized by the form of the movement, called them *Instinkthandlungen*, thereby greatly narrowing the concept of instinctive act. This use of the term gives rise to continuous misunderstandings and hence should be dropped.

The centres of this lower type of movement rarely respond to the external stimulus situation alone. As a rule, they get their internal impulses from a superordinated centre. The activation of these higher centres may result either in a mere increase in readiness of the animal to react with one of a number of consummatory actions, or, more often, in a type of movement often called 'random movement,' 'exploratory behaviour,' 'seeking behaviour,' or the like. Contrary to the consummatory action it is not characterized by a stereotyped motor pattern, but rather by (1) its variability and plasticity, and (2) its purposiveness. The animal in which a major drive, like the hunting drive, the nest-building drive, the mating drive, is activated starts searching or exploratory excursions which last until a situation is found which provides the animal with the stimuli adequate for releasing the consummatory act.

As mentioned above, Craig recognized

these two types of behaviour, viz. the variable striving behaviour and the rigid consummatory action; and, moreover, he saw their mutual relationships as components of instinctive behaviour as a whole. He called the introductory striving or searching phase 'appetitive behaviour' to stress the fact that the animal is striving to attain some end.

Appetitive behaviour may be a very simple introduction to a consummatory action, as in the case of a frog catching a prey; the preparatory taxis (turning towards the prey) is true purposive behaviour, and is continued or repeated until the prey is within range and in the median plane.

More complicated is the appetitive phase of feeding in a *Planaria* mounting a stream against a scent-loaded current.

Heinroth (1910) describes a still higher form of appetitive behaviour in mated ducks exploring the country for a nesting-hole.

In extreme cases the appetitive behaviour may be prolonged and highly adaptable, as in the migratory behaviour of animals.

It will be clear, therefore, that this distinction between appetitive behaviour and consummatory act separates the behaviour as a whole into two components of entirely different character. The consummatory act is relatively simple; at its most complex, it is a chain of reactions, each of which may be a simultaneous combination of a taxis and a fixed pattern. But appetitive behaviour is a true purposive activity, offering all the problems of plasticity, adaptiveness, and a complex integration that baffles the scientist in his study of behaviour as a whole. Appetitive behaviour is a conglomerate of many elements of very different order, of reflexes, of simple patterns like locomotion, of conditioned reactions, of 'insight' behaviour, and so on. As a result it is a true challenge to objective science, and therefore the discrimination between appetitive behaviour and consummatory act is but a first step of our analysis.

A consideration of the relationships between appetitive behaviour and consummatory act is important for our understanding of the nature of striving in animals. It is often stressed that animals are striving towards the attainment of a certain end or goal. Lorenz has pointed out not only that purposiveness, the striving towards an end, is typical only of appetitive behaviour and not of consummatory actions, but also that the end of purposive behaviour is not the attainment of an object or a situation itself, but the performance of the consummatory action, which is attained as a consequence of the animal's arrival at an external situation which provides the special sign stimuli releasing the consummatory act. Even psychologists who have watched hundreds of rats running a maze rarely realize that, strictly speaking, it is not the litter or the food the animal is striving towards, but the performance itself of the maternal activities or eating.

Holzapfel (1940) has shown that there is one apparent exception to this rule: appetitive behaviour may also lead to rest or sleep. As I hope to show further below, this exception is only apparent, because rest and sleep are true consummatory actions, dependent on activation of a centre exactly as with other consummatory actions.

Whereas the consummatory act seems to be dependent on the centres of the lowest level of instinctive behaviour, appetitive behaviour may be activated by centres of all the levels above that of the consummatory act. As has been pointed out by Baerends (1941), appetitive behaviour by no means always leads directly to the performance of a consummatory act. For instance, the hunting of a peregrine falcon usually begins with relatively random roaming around its hunting territory, visiting and exploring many different places miles apart. This first phase of appetitive behaviour may lead to different ways of catching prey, each dependent on special stimulation by a potential prey. It is continued until such a special stimulus situation is found; a flock of teal executing flight manoeuvres, a sick gull swimming apart from the flock, or even a running mouse. Each of these situations may cause the falcon to abandon its 'random' searching. But what follows then is not yet a consummatory action, but appetitive behaviour of a new, more specialized and more restricted kind. The flock of teal releases a series of sham attacks serving to isolate one or a few individuals from the main body of the flock. Only after this is achieved is the final swoop released, followed by capturing, killing, plucking, and eating, which is a relatively simple and stereotyped chain of consummatory acts. The sick gull may provoke the release of sham attacks tending to force it to fly up, if this fails the falcon may deftly pick it up from the water surface. A small mammal may release simple straightforward approach and subsequent capturing, etc. Thus we see that the generalized appetitive behaviour was continued until a special stimulus situation interrupted the random searching and released one of several possible and more specific types of appetitive behaviour. This in its turn was continued until the changing stimulus situation released the swoop, a still more specific type of appetitive behaviour, and this finally led to the chain of consummatory acts.

Baerends (1941) came to the same conclusion in his analysis of the behaviour of the digger wasp Ammophila campestris and probably the principle will be found to be generally applicable. It seems, therefore, that the centres of each level of the hierarchical system control a type of appetitive behaviour. This is more generalized in the higher levels and more restricted or more specialized in the lower levels. The transition from higher to lower, more specialized types of appetitive behaviour is brought about by special stimuli which alone are able to direct the impulses to one of the lower centres, or rather to allow them free passage to this lower centre. This stepwise descent of the activation from relatively higher to relatively lower centres eventually results in the stimulation of a centre or a series of centres of the level of the consummatory act, and here the impulse is finally used up.

This hypothesis of the mechanism of instinctive behaviour, though supported by relatively few and very fragmentary facts and still tentative therefore, seems to cover the reality better than any theory thus far advanced. Its concreteness gives it a higher heuristic value, and it is to be hoped that continued research in the near future will follow these lines and fill in, change, and adapt the sketchy frame.

Neurophysiological Facts

THE RELATIVELY HIGHER LEVELS

The hypothesis presented above, of a hierarchical system of nerve centres each of which has integrative functions of the 'collecting and redispatching' type has been developed on a foundation of facts of an indirect nature. If it is essentially right, it should be possible to trace these centres by applying neurophysiological methods. As I have said before, it must be considered as one of the greatest advantages of objective behaviour study that by using essentially the same method as other fields of physiology it gives rise to concrete problems that can be tackled by both the ethologist and the physiologist.

Now in recent times several facts have been brought to light which indicate that there is such a system of centres, at least in vertebrates.

I have already mentioned the fact that the work of Weiss, von Holst, Gray, Lissmann, and others proves that the spinal cord of fishes and amphibians must contain mechanisms controlling relatively simple types of co-ordinated movements, such as the locomotory contraction waves of the trunk muscles in fish or the locomotory rhythm of alternating contraction of leg muscles in axolotls. And although doubts have been raised concerning the absolute independence of these centres from external stimulation, the integrative, co-ordinative nature of the movements controlled by the motor centres is beyond doubt.

Other evidence of the same sort is given by the work of Adrian and Buvtendijk (1931) on the respiratory centre in the medulla of fish.

However, all these facts concern the very lowest type of centre we have postulated, that of the consummatory action or, more probably still, that of its least complex component, the fixed pattern.

Now it seems to me to be of the highest importance that recently Hess (1943, 1944; Hess and Brügger, 1943, 1944; Brügger,

1943) has succeeded, by application of strictly local artificial stimuli, to elicit behaviour of a much higher level of integration. Hess succeeded in bringing minute electrodes into the diencephalon of intact cats. In this way he would apply weak stimuli to localized parts of the brain. By systematically probing the hypothalamic region he found areas where the application of a stimulus elicited the complete behaviour patterns of either fighting, eating, or sleep. His descriptions make it clear that all the elements of the pattern were not only present but were displayed in perfect coordination. Moreover, the response was initiated by genuine appetitive behaviour; the cat looked around and searched for a corner to go to sleep, it searched for food, etc. By combining this experiment with anatomical study the position of the centres of these patterns could be determined.

These results are of considerable interest in two respects.

First, Hess appears to have found the anatomical basis of the centres controlling instinctive patterns as a whole. A mere electric shock, surely a very simple type of stimulation, releases a complex pattern, an integrated whole of movements of the highest instinctive level. This lends support to our conclusion that somewhere between receptors and effectors there must be a mechanism that takes qualitatively different, configurational impulse-patterns coming from the receptors, combines them in a purely quantitative way, and takes care of redispatching them in a re-integrative form so that a configurational movement results. Hess seems to have hit a station somewhere in this mechanism.

Second, the location of these centres is of interest in connexion with the findings about the functions of the spinal cord discussed above. While the spinal cord and the medulla seem to control only certain components of the instinctive patterns, the hypothalamus contains the highest centres concerned with instinctive behaviour. Our analysis of the hierarchical layout of behaviour patterns justifies the prediction that further research along the lines initiated by von Holst, Weiss, Gray, and Hess will lead to the discovery of a whole system of centres belonging to levels below the hypothalamic level as found by Hess, centres which are subordinate to the hypothalamic centres but which in their turn control centres lower still.

I should like to emphasize that this future work could only be done by workers who are fully acquainted with the instinctive behaviour as a whole and with its analysis, and at the same time are in command of neurophysiological methods and techniques. Our science is suffering from a serious lack of students with these qualifications, and it is an urgent task of ethologists and neurophysiologists to join efforts in the training of 'etho-physiologists.'

It is specially interesting that the hierarchical organization has not only been found in vertebrates but in insects as well. According to Baerends's results a wasp with a decentralized system of ventral ganglia and its relatively small 'brain' presents essentially the same picture as vertebrates.

INSTINCT AND INSTINCTS

The recognition of the hierarchical organization raises some problems of terminology. There is an enormous confusion around the use of the terms 'instinctive activity' or 'instinctive act.' Some authors maintain that instinctive behaviour is highly variable and adaptive in relation to a goal—in other words that it is purposive or directive—and that, because the goal remains constant while the movements, and hence the mechanisms employed, change, it is futile to attack instinctive behaviour with physiological methods. We have seen that this only applies to the appetitive part of behaviour, and moreover, that even in this purposive element of behaviour the number of possible movements and hence the number of available mechanisms is restricted. Other authors stress the rigidity, the stereotypy of instinctive behaviour.

Now it seems that the degree of variability depends entirely on the level considered. The centres of the higher levels do control purposive behaviour which is adaptive with regard to the mechanisms it employs to attain the end. The lower levels, however, give rise to increasingly simple and more stereotyped movements, until at the level of the consummatory act we have to do with an entirely rigid component, the fixed pattern, and a more or less variable component, the taxis, the variability of which, however, is entirely dependent on changes in the outer world. This seems to settle the controversy, the consummatory act is rigid, the higher patterns are purposive and adaptive. The dispute about whether 'instinctive behaviour' is rigid or adaptive has been founded on the implicit and entirely wrong assumption that there is only one type of instinctive activity.

The fact that the controversy is settled does not, of course, mean that the problem of purposiveness is solved. But the fact that even purposive behaviour appears to be dependent on quantitative activation of a centre and that it comes to an end whenever one of the lower centres has used the impulses shows that purposiveness as such is not a problem which cannot be studied by physiological methods. The fundamental problem is not to be found in the physiological mechanisms now responsible for purposive behaviour but in the history, the genesis of the species.

Returning now to our nomenclatural difficulty, the question naturally arises, What is to be called an instinctive act? Is it the pattern as a whole, or is it one of the partial patterns, or even, as Lorenz has proposed, the consummatory act? I would prefer to apply the name to all levels. For instance, reproductive behaviour in the male stickleback is, as a whole, an instinctive activity. But its component parts, nest-building and fighting, may also be called instinctive activities. A solution could be found by distinguishing instinctive acts of, for example, the first level, the second level, and so on. But here we meet with the additional difficulty that most probably the various major instinctive patterns of a species do not have the same number of levels. If we begin to count from the highest level, we would come to the absurd situation that various consummatory acts, though perhaps of the same degree of complexity, do not belong to the same level. If we begin at the level of the consummatory act, the major instincts would get different rank. This state of affairs renders it impossible to devise a universal nomenclature of instinctive behaviour as long as our knowledge is still in this fragmentary state.

It is of great importance for our understanding of instinctive behaviour as a whole to realize that the various instincts are not independent of each other. We have rejected the reflex hypothesis of behaviour and we have seen that each instinctive mechanism is constantly primed, that is to say, prepared to come into action. Such a system can only work because blocking mechanisms prevent the animal from performing continuous chaotic movements.

Now chaos is further prevented by another principle, viz. that of inhibition between centres of the same level. As a rule, an animal can scarcely do 'two things at a time.' Although there is a certain amount of synchronous activity of two instincts, this is only possible at low motivation, and, as a rule, the strong activation of instinctive behaviour of one kind prevents the functioning of another pattern. Thus an animal in which the sexual drive is strong is much less than normally susceptible to stimuli that normally release flight or eating. On the other hand, when flight is released, the thresholds of the reproductive and feeding activities are raised. The same relationship of mutual inhibition seems to exist between centres of lower levels. Intensive nest-building, for instance, renders the male stickleback much less susceptible than usual to stimuli normally releasing fighting, and vice versa.

Although the physiological basis of this inhibitory relationship will not be discussed here, it should be pointed out that its very existence has been the implicit origin of the distinction between various 'instincts' which has been made by numerous authors. So far, many authors who accepted a distinction between different instincts have defined them in terms of the goal or purpose they serve. A consideration of the neurophysiological relationships underlying instinct leads to a definition of 'an instinct' in which the responsible nervous centres and their mutual inhibition are also taken into account. It makes us realize that the purposiveness of any instinct is safeguarded by the fact that all the activities forming part of a purposive behaviour pattern aimed at the attainment of a certain goal depend on a common neurophysiological mechanism. Thus it is only natural that any definition of 'an instinct' should include not only an indication of the objective aim or purpose it is serving, but also an indication of the neurophysiological mechanisms. Because of the highly tentative character of my picture of these neurophysiological relationships it may seem a little early to attempt a definition of 'an instinct'; yet in my opinion, such an attempt could be of value for future research. I will tentatively define an instinct as a hierarchically organized nervous mechanism which is susceptible to certain priming, releasing and directing impulses of internal as well as of external origin, and which responds to these impulses of internal as well as of external origin, and which responds to these impulses by coordinated movements that contribute to the maintenance of the individual and the species.

For the same reason, it seems too early to attempt an enumeration of the various instincts to be found in animals and man. First, while we know that, in the cat, eating, fighting, and sleep must each be called a major instinct because each is dependent on the activation of a hypothalamic centre. There are patterns which almost certainly are equally dependent on a relatively high centre (e.g., escape, sexual behaviour, etc.) but of which nothing of the kind has yet been proved. Further, different species have different instincts. For instance, while many species have a parental instinct, others never take care of their offspring and hence probably do not have the corresponding neurophysiological mechanisms. However, such things are difficult to decide at present, because, for instance, it has been found that males of species in which the care of the young is exclusively an affair of the female can be brought to display the full maternal behaviour pattern by injecting them with prolactin. Though this example concerns individuals of the same species, we could not reject a priori the possibility that, for instance, a species might lack a certain instinct because, having lost it relatively recently, it retained the nervous mechanism but not the required motivational mechanism. So long as we know nothing about such things, it would be as well to refrain from generalizations.

However, it is possible to point out some inconsistencies in the present views on instincts to be found in the literature. Contrary to current views, there is, in my opinion, no 'social instinct' in our sense. There are no special activities to be called 'social' that are not part of some instinct. There is no such thing as the activation of a system of centres controlling social activities. An animal is called social when it strives to be in the neighbourhood of fellow members of its species when performing some, or all, of its instinctive activities. In other words, when these instincts are active, the fellow member of the species is part of the adequate stimulus situation which the animal tries to find through its appetitive behaviour. In some species all instincts, even the reproductive instinct and the instinct of sleep, have social aspects. In many other species the social aspect, while present in feeding or in all non-reproductive instincts, is absent from the reproductive instinct. This is especially obvious in many fishes and birds. In many amphibians the situation is just the reverse. Further, in many species there are differences of degree, or even of quality, between the social elements of different instincts. For instance, in herring gulls there is a tendency to nest in colonies. But in mating and nest-building there is only a weak social tendency, limited to the fact that individuals select their nesting site in the neighbourhood of an existing colony. Attacking a predator, one of the other sub-instincts of the reproductive instinct, is a more social affair.

There is no instinct for the selection of the environment, no *Funktionskreis des Milieus* as von Uexküll (1921) claims. Here again reactions to habitat are parts of the reproductive instinct or of other instincts.

There is, however, an instinct of sleep. Sleep is a readily recognizable, though simple behaviour pattern and has a corresponding appetitive behaviour pattern; further, it is dependent on the activation of a centre. Moreover, sleep can appear as a displacement activity (see following paragraph in this book), a property found in true instinctive patterns only.

There is, further, an instinct of comfort, or rather of care of the surface of the body.

There is not one instinct of combat. There are several sub-instincts of fighting. The most common type of fighting is sexual fighting, which is part of the reproductive pattern. Sexual fighting has to be distinguished from defence against a predator, for it has a different IRM and, often, a different motor pattern.

XIV

Until recently, attempts to explain the organization of insect societies in mechanistic terms have progressed slowly. The reason is that much of the "spirit of the hive" is invisible—a complex of chemical signals whose identities have just begun to be revealed by a combination of chemical analyses and close study of exocrine glands.

It is now believed that most communication in social insects is chemical, and that pheromone systems—the chemical signals used in communication among members of the same species—have reached their highest evolutionary development in these insects.

In the following article, Edward O. Wilson describes the investigation of pheromones for communication among bees, and the effect of these signals on their social organization. The pheromones studied to date have been mostly of two kinds: those that are ingested to influence caste and those that are transmitted in volatile form through the air to attract or alarm. There is a third category—the "surface pheromones," which are of fundamental importance to social organization, but which are extremely difficult to study because of the typically complex and delicate stimulus context in which they are found. As Mr. Wilson points out, a real breakthrough in knowledge of social insects will come when suitable extraction techniques or sufficient information on pheromone chemistry is available to understand these surface pheromones.

Chemical Communication in the Social Insects

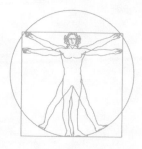

In his famous lyric work, *The Life of the Bee*, published in 1901, Maurice Maeterlinck imagined the existence of an intangible social force that directs the activity of the colony. "Where is this 'spirit of the hive' . . ." he asked, "where does it reside? . . . It disposes pitilessly of the wealth and the happiness, the liberty and life, of all this winged people; and yet with discretion, as though governed itself by some great duty." Perhaps entomologists never accepted this *élan social*, yet until quite recently their attempts to explain the organization of insect societies in mechanistic terms have gone slowly. The reason is that much of the "spirit of the hive" is actually invisible—a complex of chemical signals whose identities we have only now begun to reveal by the combination of chemical analyses and detailed studies of exocrine glands. Today this subject invites closer attention, because, in the first place, as I will argue shortly, most communication in social insects appears to be chemical, while, in the second place, pheromone systems have evidently reached their highest evolutionary development in these insects.

A chemical signal used in communication among members of the same species is called a *pheromone*, a term coined in 1959 as a substitute for the older, self-contradictory *ectohormone*.[1] Pheromones may be classified as olfactory or oral according to the site of their reception. Also, their various actions can be distinguished as releaser effects, comprising the classical stimulus-response mediated wholly by the nervous system (the stimulus being thus by definition a chemical "releaser" in ethological terminology), or primer effects, in which endocrine and reproductive systems are altered physiologically.[2] In the latter case, the body is in a sense "primed" for new biological activity, and it responds afterward with an altered behavorial repertory when presented with appropriate stimuli.

The individual social insect, in comparison with the individual solitary insect, displays behavioral patterns that are neither exceptionally ingenious nor exceptionally complex. The remarkable qualities of social life are mass phenomena that emerge from the meshing of these simple individual patterns by means of communication. If communication itself is first treated as a discrete phenomenon, the entire subject becomes much more readily analyzed. To date we have found it convenient to recognize about nine categories of responses, as follows: alarm, simple attraction, recruitment, grooming (including assistance at moulting), exchange of oral and anal liquid (the "trophallaxis" of the older literature), exchange of solid food particles, facilitation, recognition (of both nest mates and members of various castes), and caste determination either by inhibition or by stimulation.[3] Each of these kinds of responses has been shown to require chemical signals to some degree in at least some species of social insects. Most of them appear to be evoked largely or entirely by such signals. The importance of tactile and auditory stimuli in phenomena such as the waggle dance and queen piping in honey bees need not be minimized. Yet a growing amount of evidence (for a partial summary see figure 1 and table 1) now suggests that phero-

mones have the central role in the organization of insect societies.

The Alarm Substances

A case in point is the alarm response. It was natural for earlier students of behavior, who relied on simple visual observation, to conclude that alarm spreads through colonies on waves of sound and agitated movement. Sounds transmitted through the substratum can initiate alarm, but it is now apparent that the response is communicated among individuals in large part, and in some species entirely, by the discharge of certain volatile glandular secretion. Alarm, which is the normal response to intruders within the nest premises, typically consists of swift oriented movement. Some castes, or entire colonies or species, are passive, retreating into the interior of the nest or, in extremity, abandoning the nest altogether. Workers of many other species are aggressive, literally throwing their lives away in the famed altruistic manner of social insects. The responses characteristic of a given caste can be produced by presentation of the contents of certain glands, in the absence of other stimuli; happily, this provides a swift and uncomplicated bioassay. This finding, together with the simple structure of the pheromone molecules, has made the chemical identification of many of the alarm substances a straightforward task.

In the literature, *alarm* is often used synonymously with *recruitment*, and in some cases the two phenomena are indeed the same. Stuart showed that in *Zootermopsis nevadensis* (Hagen), a lower termite species, odor trails generated from the sternal gland are laid to breaks in the nest wall;[4] recruited workers assist in repelling

TABLE 1. Glandular source, chemical identity, and function of pheromones in the worker caste in the honey bee (*Apis mellifera*) and in several species of ants (Formicidae). The numbers in parentheses are literature citations. A question mark indicates that the social function of the gland, if any, is unknown; a zero indicates that the insect does not have the gland in question.

Species	Mandibular glands	Hypopharyngeal glands	Labial glands	Nassanoff's gland	Hindgut	Dufour's gland	Poison gland	Glands of sting chamber	Pavan's gland	Anal gland
					Source					
Apidae										
Apis mellifera L.	2-Heptanone: alarm[35]	Royal jelly: digestion[36]	Cleaning and dissolving[37]	Geraniol, citral, geranic acid, nerolic acid: attraction[38,39]	?	?	?	Isoamyl acetate: alarm[40]	0	0
Formicidae: Ponerinae										
Termitopone laevigata (Fr. Smith)	?	?	?	0	Trail[41]	?	?	0	0	0
Paraponera clavata (Fabr.)	Alarm[42]	?	?	0	?	?	?	0	0	0
Formicidae: Dorylinae										
Eciton spp.	Alarm[42] ?	?	Nomadic behavior?[43]	0	Trail[44]	?	?	0	0	0
Formicidae: Myrmicinae										
Solenopsis saevissima (Fr. Smith)	Alarm[5]	?	?	0	?	Trail[5]	?	0	0	0
Atta spp.	Citral: alarm[45]	?	?	0	?	?	Trail[46]	0	0	0
Tetramorium guineense (Fabr.)	?	?	?	0	?	?	Trail[47]	0	0	0
Formicidae: Dolichoderinae										
Iridomyrmex spp.	?	?	?	0	?	?	?	0	Trail[6]	2-Heptanone: alarm[48]
Tapinoma sessile (Say)	?	?	?	0	?	?	?	0	Trail[6]	Methylheptenone: alarm[6]

Species	Substance									
Formicidae: Formicinae *Acanthomyops claviger* (Roger)	Citronellal, citral: alarm[49]	?	?	?	?	o	?	?	o	o
Lasius fuliginosus (Latreille)	β(4:8-dimethyl-nona-37 dienyl) furan ("dendrolasin"): alarm?[11]	?	Trail[50]	Alarm[12]	?	o	?	o	o	
Formica polyctena (Foerster)	Alarm[12]	?	Larval and queen food[51]	?	Alarm[12]	Alarm[12]	o	o	o	

invaders and repairing the breaks. In the higher termites, which forage outside the nests, the trails are employed to recruit workers to new food sources. Stuart theorized that, in termite evolution, alarm recruitment was gradually extended to foraging recruitment, as the nests themselves no longer sufficed for food. In some ant species—for example, *Pogonomyrmex badius* (Latreille) and *Iridomyrmex pruinosus* (Roger)—alarm secretions act as attractants at low concentrations, as releasers of alarm and attack behavior at high concentrations. In the fire ant *Solenopsis saevissima* (Fr. Smith), on the other hand, an unidentified cephalic substance causes unorientated alarm behavior at both low and high concentrations; in other words, it is an alarm pheromone but not an attractant.[5]

The number of alarm substances that have been identified is greater than the number of all other identified pheromones. This is partly due to the fact that many alarm substances are volatile, produce conspicuous odors, and are stored in easily accessible glandular reservoirs. It is also due in part to the typically small size and structural simplicity of the molecules. Besides the substances listed in table 1, with which behavioral tests have been performed, various elementary aldehydes and ketones which may be performing an alarm function have been identified from other ant species. These include methylheptenone and propyl isobutyl ketone in *Tapinoma nigerrima* (Nylander)—compounds which are exciters of alarm behavior in the related *T. sessile* (Say);[6] methylheptenone in Australian species of *Iridomyrmex* and *Dolichoderus*;[7] methylhexanone in *Acanthoclinea clarki* Wheeler;[7] 2-hexenal in *Crematogaster afri-*

cana Mayr,[8] and limonene in *Myrmicaria natalensis* (Fr. Smith).[9]

Bossert and I predicted, on the basis of a priori considerations of potential molecular diversity in the pheromones and of olfactory efficiency in insect chemoreceptors, that most alarm substances would prove to have between five and ten carbon members and to have molecular weights between 100 and 200.[2] The very limited species specificity known to prevail in substances with molecules in this size range could be attained by the available diversity in molecular structure. We also concluded that in order for a substance to have a short fading time—a necessary property for an efficient alarm system—an intermediate response-threshold concentration, neither very high nor very low, is needed. Insect chemoreceptors appear to have been so constructed in the course of evolution as to respond with increasing efficiency to molecules of increasing size in a homologous series. They are capable of being very efficiently adjusted to volatile odorants with molecular weights in the 100-to-200 range. The properties of alarm communication have been investigated quantitatively in *Pogonomyrmex badius*. By directly measuring the effects of alarm substances from whole crushed heads, we obtained estimates for the "Q/K ratio"—the ratio of (i) pheromone molecules released to (ii) response-threshold concentrations (in molecules per cubic centimeter)—ranging between 939 and 1800. The threshold concentration was then indirectly estimated to be about 5×10^{13} molecules per cubic centimeter. The Q/K ratio for these alarm substances falls far below the ratios calculated for the sex attractants of moths and is well above those for the trail substance of fire ants.[10] In agreement with

these parameters, the entire contents of the paired mandibular glands of *P. badius* provides a brief signal when discharged in air. A small "active space" (that is, space within which the concentration is at or above the response threshold) is generated, attaining a maximum radius of only about 6 centimeters. After approximately 35 seconds, further diffusion reduces the active space to nearly zero, and the signal vanishes. The *Pogonomyrmex* colony is thus able to localize its alarm communication sharply in time and space.

The rule that alarm substances have small, relatively simple molecules has continued to hold since we first formulated it in 1962. At that time there seemed to be one conspicuous exception. Dendrolasin, a furan with a molecular weight of 218, found in the mandibular glands of *Lasius fuliginosus*, was said by its discoverer M. Pavan to cause an alarm response in *L. fuliginosus* workers.[11] However, later quantitative assays by Maschwitz show that, in this species, the alarm substances are concentrated in Dufour's gland, while the mandibular glands are relatively inactive.[12] Synthetic dendrolasin has not to my knowledge been assayed quantitatively, and large doses may well cause the alarm effect reported by Pavan.

Although cataloging of the alarm substances has only begun, three of them—citral, 2-heptanone, and methylheptenone—have already been found in more than one species of social hymenopteran. This discovery is not surprising in view of the simplicity of the molecular structure. The range of candidate substances must have been further narrowed by requirements of diffusivity and by probable limitations in the biosynthetic capacity of the insects.

At least some of the pheromones serve also as defensive secretions. Roth and Eisner report that citronellal facilitates the penetration of formic acid into the cuticle of enemy arthropods.[13] Maschwitz claims that formic acid itself, long known to be a primary defensive secretion in formicine ants, serves as a secondary alarm pheromone in *Formica polyctena* Foerster.[12] Pinenes manufactured in the cephalic glands of nasute soldiers of the termite genus *Nasutitermes* probably serve both in defense and in the communication of alarm.[14] It seems appropriate that the two functions, which are required simultaneously in times of danger, should be served by the same substances. The question remains, Which function was served first in the evolution of particular phyletic lines?

The Caste Pheromones

Building upon the early experimental work of A. L. Pickens in 1932 and E. M. Miller and S. F. Light in the 1940's, Martin Lüscher and his associates have developed a picture of remarkably complex and precise pheromonal caste control in the termites. Much of the information concerning specific inferred substances is given in figure 1. In *Kalotermes flavicollis* (Fabricius), the species of Lüscher's study, the key caste is the pseudergate, a large nymph-like stage that performs the tasks of the worker in other insect societies and is capable, when the inhibitory pheromones are removed, of transforming into a soldier or one of the two reproductive castes. It has become clear that the pheromones act by interfering with the endocrine system. In particular, the proportion of orphaned pseudergates that change into replacement reproductives

shows a negative correlation with the volume of the corpora allata, while soldiers can be produced experimentally from pseudergates by implantation of the corpora allata of reproductives.[15] However, neither the responsible hormones of the corpora allata nor their exact modes of action have been elucidated. Also, to date, none of the caste-controlling pheromones have been chemically identified.

It is likely that patterns of caste control vary greatly within the termites as a whole. *Zootermopsis* and *Kalotermes*, in which pheromones have been demonstrated, are primitive genera. In the higher Termitidae, phylogenetically the most advanced group of all the termites, reproductives can be derived only from nymphs. A true worker caste exists which lacks the potential for caste alteration.[16]

When the mother queen of a honey bee colony is removed, the workers respond in as short a time as 30 minutes by changing from a state of organized activity to one of disorganized restlessness. In a few more hours, they begin to alter one or more worker brood cells into emergency queen cells, within which a new nest queen is eventually produced. A few days later, some of the workers begin to experience increased ovarian development. These combined releaser and primer effects were known, as early as 1954, to be due to the removal of a pheromone present in the queen, called "queen substance" by C. G. Butler.[17] Now it appears that at least two inhibitory pheromones are involved in these effects. Moreover, the special treatment accorded the queen is due to at least two additional attractive scents.[18,19]

One of the inhibitory pheromones present in the queen honey bee is *trans*-9-keto-

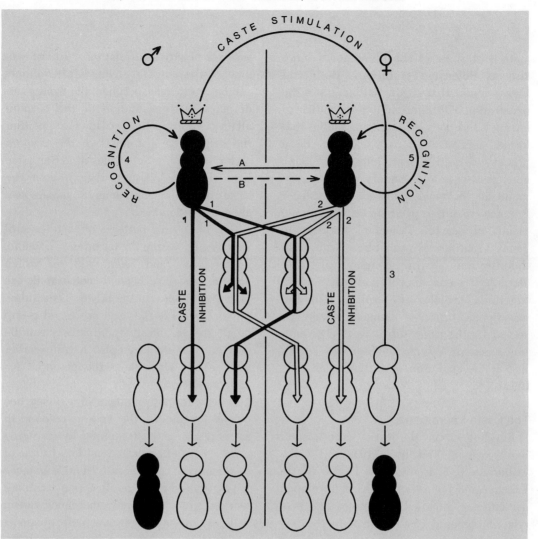

Figure 1 *The known pathways of pheromone action in the control of reproductive caste formation in the termite Kalotermes flavicollis. (Top row) Pair of figures representing the "royal" reproductives; (remaining rows) figures representing pseudergates. The king and queen produce substances (labeled 1 and 2, respectively) which inhibit development of pseudergates into their own royal castes. These inhibitory pheromones are passed directly from the reproductives to the pseudergates and are also circulated indirectly through the digestive tracts of the pseudergates. Another male substance (pheromone 3) stimulates the female pseudergates to transform to the reproductive caste, but the reverse relation does not hold. When supernumerary royal males are present, they recognize each other (through pheromone 4) and fight; similarly, supernumerary royal females recognize each other (through peromone 5) and fight. Finally, royal males stimulate production of pheromone 2 in royal females, and royal females stimulate production of pheromone 1 in royal males; the nature of the stimuli, which are labeled A and B, is unknown.* [*After Lüscher*[54]]

2-decenoic acid. This substance was characterized in 1960 by Butler, Callow, and Johnston in England and, at the same time, by Barbier and Lederer in France.[20,21] It is produced entirely in the queen's man- dibular glands. Its odor alone is sufficient to inhibit to some extent both queen-rearing behavior and ovary development in worker bees. It works in conjunction with a second inhibitory scent produced in a part of the body outside the mandibular glands. When experimentally injected into the body cavity of the worker, thus by-passing the external chemoreceptors, it continues to inhibit ovary development but not queen-rearing behavior.[22] Lüscher and Walker found that the corpora allata of workers increase in size for the first few days following removal of the queen, and they have hypothesized that the inhibitory pheromones act by suppressing secretion of the "gonadotropic" hormone.[23] Whether the pheromones produce their effects by direct action on the corpora allata or indirectly through a more circuitous route in the central nervous system remains to be learned.

A paradox was raised by the early findings on inhibition by "queen substance": How can a normal colony produce new queens in the annual breeding season in the presence of the mother queen? The solution has been obtained by Butler.[24] By appropriate experiments, he first excluded the hypothesis that the attractiveness of "queen substance" is greater for pre-swarm workers than for workers from nonswarming colonies. Then he determined that the amount of "queen substance" (as measured by the inhibiting power of whole-body extracts) in mother queens from colonies involved in normal reproduction, by means of swarming, is only about one quarter that of mother queens from nonreproducing-colonies.

Similarly acting inhibitory pheromones have recently been located in the heads of queens of the ant genus *Myrmica*.[25] It is thus proved that each of the most advanced groups of the social insects—the termites, the honey bees, and the ants—has evolved pheromonal control by the queen. In groups with less distinct caste systems, the control devices are more crude and direct. In some wasps of the genus *Polistes* and some bumble bees of the genus *Bombus* the queen differs only slightly in appearance from other adult females of the colony. She dominates them by threat behavior and, in addition, appears to bear a distinctive odor recognized by her subordinates.[26] In the quite primitively social *Lasioglossum zephytum* (Smith), some degree of reproductive domination is achieved by females who remove eggs of rivals from brood cells and substitute their own.[27] Evolution of reproductive control in social insects can be interpreted as having consisted of a transition from direct intervention among rival females utilizing recognition scents to indirect control by means of directed worker behavior and primer pheromones.

The Increase of Information

An individual pheromone is capable of communicating far more information than the maximum single unit (the "bit") implicit in a simple on-or-off signal. The parameters of diffusion rate, emission rate, and response threshold have clearly been evolved in animal species to permit both localization of the source in space and an appropriate fading time.[2] The actual information transmitted has been measured in the case of the odor trail of the fire ant (*Solenopsis saevissima*). When worker ants find a new food source or a superior nest site, they run homeward, laying a trail consisting of minute traces of Dufour's gland secretion. The secretion is a volatile attractant. As it diffuses in still air it forms a semi-ellipsoidal active space whose transverse maximum radius is only about 1 centimeter. During the lifetime of the active space—approximately 100 seconds when the trail is laid on a nonabsorbing surface—recruited workers run away from the nest while orienting themselves to remain inside the space. If they are able to keep this up long enough they arrive in the vicinity of the "target." By recording the points at which responding workers turn back to the nest or lose the trail, I was able to measure response errors with reference to the target from which the trail had been drawn. These statistics were then translated into information measures, with the results shown in figure 2. Although the amount of directional information increases with the length of the trail (due to the nearly constant diameter of the ellipsoidal active space throughout its length), the rate of information transmission drops off because of the disproportionately in-

creasing period of time required to lay and follow the trail. Even so, both the total amount of information transmitted and the transmission rate are considerable; the amount of directional information, for example, is comparable to that transmitted by the waggle dance of the honey bee.

The fading time of a chemical signal can easily be adjusted, in the course of evolution, by altering the Q/K ratio, the emission rate, or both. In the case of ingested pheromones, it might conceivably also be shortened by enzymatic deactivation of the molecules. Just such a mechanism in the case of *trans*-9-keto-2-decenoic acid has recently been discovered by Johnston, Law, and Weaver.[28] These investigators traced the metabolism of a radioactive form of the

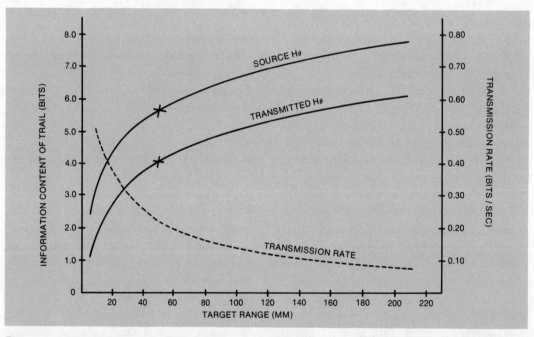

Figure 2 *Information content and transmission rate with reference to direction in the odor trail of the fire ant Solenopsis saevissima. (Source H$_\theta$) Curve represents the amount of information which would be transmitted if the trail were followed perfectly. (Transmitted H$_\theta$) Curve represents transmitted information, based on the actual performance of follower workers. Although the amount of information increases as the trails grow longer, the time required to lay and follow them increases disproportionately, with the result that the actual transmission rate drops off steadily.* [After Wilson[5]]

pheromone fed to worker bees and found that within 72 hours over 95 percent of it had been converted into inactive substances, consisting principally of 9-ketodecanoic acid, 9-hydroxydecanoic acid, and 9-hydroxy-2-decenoic acid. The metabolic route shown in figure 3 was then

postulated. Johnston *et al.* have further hypothesized the existence of a "pheromone cycle." The inactive molecules might be passed back to the queen as part of the regurgitated glandular queen food. The queen could then convert them into the active form by very simple enzymatic pro-

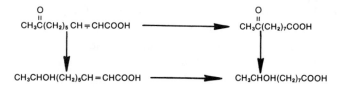

Figure 3 *Trans-9-keto-2-decenoic acid and its inactive derivatives produced within the body of the worker honey bee. After Johnston et al. (28)*

cesses, resulting in a saving to the queen of a "relatively enormous amount of energy required for the complete synthesis of the fatty acid chain." The queen, it should be added, carries only a little more than 100 micrograms of the ketodecenoic acid on her at any given moment,[19] and she must dispense on the order of 0.1 microgram of this substance per day per worker in the colony to suppress queen rearing.

So far I have emphasized adjustments of fading time and of the geometrical properties of the active space as two ways in which the information in a chemical communication system may be increased. A third device found in social insects is the employment of medleys of substances with more than one "meaning." A minimum of 32 substances have been detected in the heads of honey bee queens, including methyl 9-ketodecanoate, methyl 9-keto-2-decenoate, nonoic acid, decanoic acid, 2-decenoic acid, 9-ketodecanoic acid, 9-hydroxy-2-decenoic acid, 10-hydroxy-2-decenoic acid, 9-keto-2 decenoic acid, and others. Most or all are present in the mandibular gland secre-

tion.[29] The biological significance of most of these products is unknown. Some are undoubtedly precursors to pheromones, but at least two are known pheromones with quite contrasting effects: the 9-ketodecenoic acid is the inhibitory pheromone already mentioned, while the 9-hydroxydecenoic acid causes clustering and stabilization of worker swarms.[30]

A fourth device found in social insects for increasing information in a chemical communication system is for the same pheromone to convey different meanings in different contexts. *Trans*-9-keto-2-decenoic acid serves as a caste-inhibitory pheromone inside the honey bee nest and as the primary volatile sex attractant during the nuptial flight.[31] The Dufour's gland secretion of the fire ant *Solenopsis saevissima* is an attractant that is effective on members of all castes during most of their adult life. Under different circumstances it serves variously to recruit workers to new food sources, to organize colony emigration, and—in conjunction with a cephalic secretion—to cause alarm behavior.[5]

A fifth modification is for the insects to respond in different ways to different concentrations of a substance, and to different durations of exposure. Workers of *Pogonomyrmex badius* react to low concentrations of mandibular gland secretion by simple positive chemotaxis and to higher concentrations by typical aggressive alarm behavior. When exposed to high concentrations for more than a minute or two, many individuals switch from alarm to digging behavior.[32] The digging is directed to the source of the substance and has the result of bringing aid to injured or trapped nest mates.

In a sixth modification, pheromones acquire additional or even different meanings when they are presented in combination. When released near fire ant workers, cephalic and Dufour's gland secretions cause unoriented alarm behavior and attraction, respectively; when expelled simultaneously by a highly excited worker, they cause oriented alarm behavior.[5] Honey bee workers confined closely with queens for hours acquire scents from her which, evidently in combination with their own worker-recognition scent, cause them to be attacked by nest mates.[33] Males of the ant *Lasius neoniger* Emery discharge most of their mandibular gland contents during the nuptial flight, almost certainly as an aerial courtship signal. The glands contain 2,6-dimethyl-5-hepten-1-ol, citronellol, geraniol, and a few other simple compounds. The two species of *Lasius* and the one species of the related genus *Acanthomyops* that have been studied thus far have many mandibular gland components in common, but, perhaps as an evolutionary solution to the problem of interspecific sexual isolation, the proportions of the components in the three species differ radically.[34]

A Large Gap in Pheromone Research

If the information given here seems limited—and it certainly should, in view of the enormous diversity of social insects—it must be considered even further narrowed by the existence of a gap in our knowledge, one that is largely unappreciated. The pheromones studied in detail to date have been mostly of two kinds: those that are ingested to influence caste and those that are transmitted in volatile form through the air to attract or alarm. For various technical reasons such substances have been relatively easy to extract and bioassay. There is a third category of substances that have proved far more refractory, comprising what might be termed the "surface pheromones." These substances either are absorbed on the body surface or generate such shallow active spaces in air that they must be perceived by contact chemoreception. Indirect evidence is adequate to demonstrate their existence; in particular they are the colony odors, which include the species odors, the caste-recognition scents, the releasers of grooming behavior, and (in at least some social insects) the secretions that stimulate food exchange. Of fundamental importance to social organization, they are nevertheless extremely difficult to study because of the typically complex and delicate stimulus context in which they are found. When removed from the other surface odors or masked by alien substances that are added in conventional extraction techniques, they no longer produce behavioral effects. We do not now have suitable extraction techniques or sufficient information on pheromone chemistry to make much progress in studying surface pheromones, but, hopefully, they are not beyond our reach.

References

[1] P. Karlson and A. Butenandt, *Annu. Rev. Entomol.* 4, 39 (1959); P. Karlson and M. Lüscher, *Nature* 183, 55 (1959).

[2] E. O. Wilson and W. H. Bossert, *Recent Progr. Hormone Res.* 19, 673 (1963).

[3] M. Lindauer, *Physiology of Insecta*, M. Rockstein, Ed. (Academic Press, New York , 1965), vol. 2, p. 123.

[4] A. M. Stuart, *Nature* 189, 419 (1961); *Proc. Zool. Soc. London* 143, 43 (1964).

[5] E. O. Wilson, *Animal Behaviour* 10, 134 (1962).

[6] ———— and M. Pavan, *Psyche* 66, 79 (1959).

[7] G. W. K. Cavill and H. Hinterberger, *Proc. Intern. Congr. Entomol. 11th, London* (1960), vol. 3, p. 284.

[8] C. W. L. Bevan, A. J. Birch, H. Caswell, *J. Chem. Soc. 1961*, 488 (1961).

[9] P. Grünanger, A. Quilico, M. Pavan, *Rend. Accad. Sci. Fis. Mat. (Soc. Naz. Sci.)* 28, 293 (1960).

[10] W. H. Bossert and E. O. Wilson, *J. Theoret. Biol.* 5, 443 (1963).

[11] M. Pavan, *Atti Accad. Naz. Ital. Entomol. Rend.* 8, 228 (1961).

[12] U. Maschwitz, *Z. Vergleich. Physiol.* 47, 596 (1964).

[13] L. M. Roth and T. Eisner, *Annu. Rev. Entomol.* 7, 107 (1962).

[14] B. P. Moore, *J. Insect Physiol.* 10, 371 (1964); personal communication, April 1965.

[15] M. Lüscher, *Proc. Intern. Congr. Zool. 16th, Washington, D.C.* (1963), vol. 4, p. 244.

[16] C. Noirot, *Insectes Sociaux* 3, 145 (1956).

[17] C. G. Butler, *Trans. Roy. Entomol. Soc. London* 105, 11 (1954).

[18] ———— , *J. Insect Physiol.* 7, 258 (1961); ———— and J. Simpson, *Veda. Prirodni. Vyzkum. Ust. Zemed.* (1965), p. 33.

[19] C. G. Butler and P. N. Patton, *Proc. Roy. Entomol. Soc. London* A37, 114 (1962).

[20] C. G. Butler, R. K. Callow, N. C. Johnston, *Proc. Roy. Soc. London* B155, 417 (1961).

[21] M. Barbir and E. Lederer, *Compt. Rend.* 250, 4467 (1960).

[22] C. G. Butler and E. M. Fairey, *J. Apicultural Res.* 2, 14 (1963).

[23] M. Lüscher and I. Walker, *Rev. Suisse Zool.* 70, 304 (1963).

[24] C. G. Butler, *Proc. Roy. Entomol. Soc. London* A35, 129 (1960).

[25] M. V. Brian and J. Hibble, *J. Insect Physiol.* 9, 25 (1963).

[26] J. B. Free, *Brit. J. Animal Behaviour* 3, 147 (1955).

[27] S. W. T. Batra, *Insectes Sociaux* 11, 159 (1964).

[28] N. C. Johnston, J. H. Law, N. Weaver, *Biochemistry*, in press.

[29] R. K. Callow, J. R. Chapman, P. N. Paton, *J. Apicultural Res.* 3, 77 (1964).

[30] C. G. Butler, R. K. Callow, J. R. Chapman, *Nature* 201, 733 (1964).

[31] N. E. Gary, *Science* 136, 773 (1962); C. G. Butler and E. M. Fairey, *J. Apicultural Res.* 3, 65 (1964).

[32] E. O. Wilson, *Psyche* 65, 41 (1958).

[33] R. A. Morse and N. E. Gary, *Bee World* 42, 197 (1961).

[34] J. H. Law, E. O. Wilson, J. A. McCloskey, *Science*, in press.

[35] D. A. Shearer and R. Boch, *Nature*, in press.

[36] D. Otto, *Zool. Anz.* 161, 216 (1958).

[37] J. Simpson, *J. Insect Physiol.* 4, 107 (1960).

[38] M. Renner, *Z. Vergleich. Physiol.* 43, 411 (1960).

[39] R. Boch and D. A. Shearer, *Nature* 194, 704 (1962); ———— , *ibid.* 202, 320 (1964); N. Weaver, E. C. Weaver, J. H. Law *Progr. Rep. Texas Agr. Exp. Sta.* PR-2324 (1964).

[40] R. Boch, D. A. Shearer, B. C. Stone, *Nature* 195, 1018 (1962); R. L. Ghent and N. E. Gary, *Psyche* 69, 1 (1962).

[41] M. S. Blum, personal communication, May 1965.

[42] E. O. Wilson, *Annu. Rev. Entomol.* 8, 345 (1963).

[43] E. R. Lappano, *Insectes Sociaux* 5, 31 (1958).

[44] M. S. Blum and C. A. Portocarrero, *Ann. Entomol. Soc. Amer.* 57, 793 (1964).

[45] A. Butenandt, B. Linzen, M. Lindauer, *Arch. Anat. Microscop. Morphol. Exp.* 48, 13 (1959).

[46] J. C. Moser and M. S. Blum, *Science* 140, 1228 (1963).

[47] M. S. Blum and G. N. Ross, *J. Insect. Physiol.*, in press.

[48] M. S. Blum, S. L. Warter, R. S. Monroe, J. C. Chidester, *ibid.* 9, 881 (1963).

[49] R. L. Gent, thesis, Cornell University (1961).

[50] J. D. Carthy, *Nature* 166, 154 (1950); W. Hangartner and S. Berstein, *Experientia* 20, 396 (1964).

[51] K. Gösswald and W. Kloft, *Zool. Beitr.* 5, 519 (1960).

[52] R. Ribbands, *The Behaviour and Social Life of Honeybees* (Bee Research Association, London, 1953), p. 57.

[53] M. Pavan and G. Ronchetti, *Atti Soc. Ital. Sci. Natur. Museo Civico Storia Natur. Milano* 94, 379 (1955).

[54] M. Lüscher, *Symp. Roy. Entomol. Soc. London* 1, 57 (1961).

XV

ONE OF THE MOST persistently provocative fantasies of man has concerned interplanetary travel and contact with life from other worlds. As we contemplate the possibility of life beyond the earth, we are reminded of the still unanswered question: What is the origin of life? Wherever truth may lie, all theories on the origin of life have suffered from a lack of comparison to a nonterrestrial life system, against which they could be tested.

In the following article, Joshua Lederberg discusses the challenges implicit in extending the boundaries of biology into space (exobiology).

Exobiology: Approaches to Life Beyond the Earth

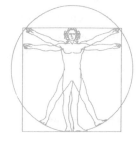

IT IS A privilege to discuss some basic problems in biology with an audience whose special concern is for the recent striking advances in the physics of the earth in the solar system. However, many of us are looking forward to the close investigation of the planets, and few inquisitive minds can fail to be intrigued by what these studies will tell of the cosmic distribution of life. To conform to the best of our contemporary science, much thoughtful insight, meticulous planning, and laboratory testing must still be invested in the experimental approaches to this problem. This may require international cooperation and also—perhaps more difficult—mutual understanding among scientific disciplines as isolated as biochemical genetics and planetary astronomy.

Many discussions of space exploration have assumed that exobiological studies might await the full development of the technology for manned space flight and for the return of planetary samples to the terrestrial laboratory. To be sure, these might be preceded by some casual experiments on some instrumented landings. One advantage of such a program is that time would allow exobiological experiments to be planned with composure and deliberation. Undoubtedly, this planning would be more rigorous insofar as it was based on improved knowledge, from closer approaches, of the chemistry and physics of planetary habitats. Unfortunately, this orderly and otherwise desirable program takes insufficient account of the capacity of living organisms to grow and spread throughout a new environment. This unique capacity of life which engages our deepest interest also generates our gravest concerns in the scientific management of missions beyond the earth. On account of these, as well as of the immense costs of interplanetary communication, we are obliged to weigh the most productive experiments that we can do by remote instrumentation in early flights, whether or not manned space flight eventually plays a role in scientific exploration.

Motivations for Exobiological Research

The demons which lurk beyond the Pillars of Hercules have colored the folklore and literature of ages past and present, not always to the benefit of fruitful exploration and dispassionate scientific analysis. Apart from such adventuresome amusements and the amateur delights of a cosmically enlarged natural history, how does exobiology relate to contemporary science and culture? The exploration of space may seem to have very little to do with fundamental questions in biology or medicine, with the role of genes in embryological development, protein synthesis, the biology of viruses, and the evolution of species. The physical sciences may sharpen our perspective. Twenty-five centuries of scientific astronomy have widened the horizons of the physical world, and the casual place of the planet Earth in the expanding universe is a central theme in our modern scientific culture. The dynamics of celestial bodies, as observed from the earth, is the richest inspiration for the generalization of our concepts of mass and energy throughout the universe. The spectra of the stars likewise testify to the universality of our concepts in chemistry. But biology has lacked tools for

such extension, and "life" until now has meant only terrestrial life. This disparity in the domains of the physical versus the biological sciences attenuates most of our efforts to construct a theoretical biology as a cognate of theoretical physics or chemistry. For the most part, biological science has been the rationalization of particular facts, and we have had all too limited a basis for the construction and testing of meaningful axioms to support a theory of life. At present, perhaps the only potentially universal principle in biology is the Darwinian concept of evolution through the natural selection of random hereditary fluctuations.

Some chemical attributes of terrestrial life might support a claim to be basic principles: for example, polyphosphates (adenylpyrophosphate) occur in all organisms as coupling agents for the storage and transfer of metabolic energy. But, at least in principle, we can imagine that organisms may have found alternative solutions to the same problem. Only the perspective of comparative biology on a cosmic scale could tell whether this device is an indispensable element of all life or a particular attribute of its local occurrence on this planet.

An important aim of theoretical biology is an abstract definition of life. Our only consensus so far is that such a definition must be arbitrary. If life has gradually evolved from inanimate matter, the demarcation of chemical from biological evolution is one of useful judgment. For a working principle, we might again rely upon the evolutionary concept: a living system has those properties (of self-replication and metabolism) from which we may with more or less confidence deduce an evolutionary scheme that would encompass self-evidently living organisms. But I do not propose this as a rote formula for the assessment of life on other celestial bodies, and certainly not before we have some empirical knowledge of the diversities of chemical evolution.

From this standpoint, the overriding objective of exobiological research is to compare the over-all patterns of chemical evolution of the planets, stressing those features which are globally characteristic of each of them.

We are all thinking of the question: "Is there life on Mars?" To answer it may require a careful reassessment of our meaning of "life" and matching this with the accumulation of hard-won evidence on the chemical composition of that planet. On the other hand, we might be confronted with an object obviously analogous to an earthly plant, animal or microbe. But even this abrupt answer would be trivial in deference to a biochemical analysis of the organism and of its habitat for comparison with the fundamentals of terrestrial life.

In our first approaches to the nearby planets we will wish to design experiments which have some tangible foundation in the present accumulation of biochemical knowledge. The aqueous environment, and its corollary of moderate temperatures in which large carbonaceous molecules are reasonably stable, are implicit in terrestrial biochemistry. This is not to reject the abstract possibility of nonaqueous life, or noncarbonaceous molecules that might characterize temperatures of $<200°$ or $>500°\,K$. However, we can defer our concern for such exotic biological systems until we have got full value from our searches for the more familiar, and have learned enough of the exotic chemistry to judge how to proceed.

Within the bounds of its aqueous environment, what are the most nearly universal features of terrestrial life? In fact, our plants, animals, and bacteria share a remarkable list of biochemical components, and a biochemist cannot easily distinguish extracts of yeast cells and beef muscle. Among these components, the nucleic acids warrant first attention. Although they constitute the hereditary material, so that all the variety of terrestrial life can be referred to subtle differences in the nucleic acids, the same basic structure is found in the nuclei of all cells. This a long, linear polymer fabricated from a sugar-phosphate repeating unit:

where R is a purine side group:

Adenine   Guanine

or a pyrimidine side group:

Thymine   Cytosine

The meaningful variety of nucleic acids depends on the specific order of the side group attached to each sugar on this monotonous backbone, a linear message written in a language of four letters, *A, G, T,* and *C*. The bacteria, which are the simplest free-living organisms, contain nucleotide sequences about 5 million units long; man contains sequences about 5000 million units long—this content being one of our best objective measures of biological complexity. On the other hand, the simplest viruses, which can multiply only inside living cells and come close to being single genes, have about 2500 units per particle. Playing a central role in the unification of terrestrial biology, nucleic acids underlie both heredity and (through their control of protein synthesis) development. Are they the only linear polymers which can subsume these functions, or have many other fundamental types evolved, to be found on other celestial bodies?

Equally general among the constituents of living cells are the proteins, which are also polymers, but with a more diverse set of constituents, some 20 amino acids. The fundamental backbone of a protein is a poly-amino acid chain:

$$H-NH-CH-CO-NH-CH-CO\ldots$$
$$R \qquad\qquad R$$
$$\ldots NH-CH-CO-OH$$
$$R$$

where *R* may be any of 20 different groups, distinguishing a like number of amino acids found in natural proteins. Proteins assume a wide variety of three-dimensional shapes, through coiling and cross-linking of the polymer chains. They are in this way suited to perform such diverse functions as those of enzymes, structural elements, and antibodies. Not only do we find just the same 20 amino acids among the proteins of all terrestrial organisms but these are all the levo-isomers, although dextro- amino acids are found to have other metabolic functions. Next only to the incidence of nucleic acids, we would ask whether exobiota make analogous use of proteins, comprising the same amino acids, in hopes of understanding what seem to be random choices in the sculpture of our own living form.

Common to all forms of terrestrial life are also a number of smaller molecules which are involved in the working metabolism of the cells; for example, most of the B vitamins have a perfectly general distribution. They are vitamins for us only because we have learned, in our evolutionary history, to rely on their production by green plants, rather than to synthesize them within our own cells. But once formed, these vitamins, and similar categories of substances such as porphyrins, play entirely analogous roles in the metabolism of all cells.

A few substances, such as the steroid hormones, do play special roles in the metabolism of higher organisms, and testify to some progress in biochemical evolution. In fact, most objective evidence points to a loss of specific functions—microorganisms are certainly more versatile and less dependent than man is on a specific nutrient mileu. The main trend of biochemical evolution, from microbe to man, has been far less the innovation of new unit processes than the coordination of existing processes in time and space.

While we propose to give first priority to

these most general questions, they by no means exhaust our interest in the peculiarities of extraterrestrial organisms, any more than they would for a newly discovered phylum of the earth's own repertoire. Nor should we preclude the possibility of finding new organisms that might be economically useful to man, just as new organisms were among the most fruitful yields of geographic exploration. However, the enlargement of our understanding, rather than of our zoos and botanical gardens, is surely our first objective.

Theories of the Origin of Life

At this point, a consideration of contemporary theory on the origin of life is justified for two reasons: (i) exobiological research gives us a unique, fresh approach to this problem, and (ii) we can find some basis to conclude that life need not be so improbable an evolutionary development as had once been supposed.

The interval between Pasteur's work on spontaneous generation and the recent past has been especially difficult for the mechanistic interpretation of the origin of life. Before Pasteur's time, many investigators could believe that simple microorganisms arose spontaneously in nutrient media. His demonstration that such media remained sterile if properly sterilized and protected seemed to rule out any possibility of "spontaneous generation." His conclusion was, of course, overdrawn, since life must have evolved at least once, and the event could still occur, though very much less frequently than had been supposed before. Meanwhile, the problem was compounded by the growth of biochemical knowledge. We now realize that bacteria, small as they are, are still extremely complex, well-or-

dered, and representative organisms. The first organisms must have been far simpler than present-day free-living bacteria.

With the growth of genetics since 1900, and the recognition of the self-replicating gene as the elementary basis of life, the question could focus on the origin of the first genetic molecule: given the power of self-replication, and incidents of stochastic variation, Darwin's principle could account for the eventual emergence of any degree of biological complexity.

An immense amount of fruitful genetic work was done in a period when "genetic molecule" was an abstraction and "self-replication" was an axiomatic principle whose chemical basis seemed beyond the grasp of human understanding. Now we recognize that the nucleic acids are the material basis of heredity, and we can begin to construct mechanistic models of their replication. The first principle, as already stated, is that the gene is a string of nucleotides, each position in the string being marked by one of the four nucleotide units A, T, C, and G. The polymerization of such strings by the union of the monomeric units presents no fundamental problems, but self-replication would necessitate the assembly of the units in a specific order, the one dictated by the order of the nucleotides in the parent molecule. The key to the solution of this problem was the realization by Watson and Crick that the complete nucleic acid molecule is a rigid, duplex structure in which two strings are united. In that rigid structure, as can be shown by suitable molecular models, adenine occupies a space which is just complementary to that of thymine, and cytosine is likewise complementary to guanine. A string can therefore replicate— that is, direct the assembly of another daughter string—in the following way. The nutrient mix of the cell contains all four nucleotide units. However, at any position of the parent nucleic acid molecule only one of these four can make a suitable fit and will therefore be accepted. After being accepted, the daughter units are firmly bound together by new chemical linkages giving a well-defined daughter string. Kornberg has reconstructed most of these events in some detail, by means of extracts from bacteria, to the very verge of proving duplication of genes in a chemically defined system in the test tube.

However, the media in which such syntheses can occur, in the cell or even in the test tube, are extremely complex. Knowing that the simplest organisms would be the most dependent on their environments for raw materials, where did these precursors come from before living organisms had evolved the enzymes to manufacture them?

Thanks to the insight of Haldane, Oparin, Horowitz and others, we now realize that this paradox is a false one, though it dates to the confusion between "carbon chemistry" and "organic chemistry" which still exists in English terminology. In fact, in 1828, Wöhler had already shown that an organic compound, urea, could be formed experimentally from an inorganic salt, ammonium cyanate. A hundred years later, a number of routes for synthesis of geochemically significant amounts of complex organic materials were pointed out, for example, the hydrolysis of metallic carbides, and subsequent reactions of olefins with water and ammonia. More recently, Miller and Urey demonstrated the actual production of amino acids by the action of electric discharges on gas mixtures containing the

hydrides NH_3, OH_2, and CH_4. This demonstration converges with other argument that the primitive atmosphere of the earth had just such a reduced composition, becoming oxidized secondarily (and in part through photo-synthetic separation of carbon from oxygen).

An alternative theory of origin of carbonaceous molecules is even more pervasive. Perhaps we associate carbon with life, and rocks and metals with physical phenomena; beyond doubt we tend to connote the latter with the predominant substance of the universe. In fact, as a glance at tables of cosmic abundance will show, the lighter elements are by far the most prevalent, and after the dispersed hydrogen and helium these are carbon, oxygen, and nitrogen. The primitive condensation of free atoms to form the interstellar smoke, and eventually the stars themselves, must entail the molecular aggregation $H + C + O + N$; that is, a large fraction of the condensed mass of the universe must consist, or once have consisted, of organic macro-molecules of great complexity. The chief problem for their synthesis is in fact not a source of chemical energy but how to dissipate the excess energy of reactions of free atoms and radicals.

This aspect of astrophysics may have place for a remote biological analogy: Once a few molecules have formed, the energy of subsequent impacts can be dissipated among the vibrational degrees of freedom. That is, such molecules can function as nuclei of condensation. As seeds for further condensation, those molecules will be favored which (i) most readily dissipate the energy of successive impacts and (ii) can undergo molecular fission to increase the number of nuclei. The actual molecular chemistry of the interstellar (or prestellar) smoke is thus subject to a kind of natural selection and cannot be a purely random sampling of available atoms.

Whether the earth has retained remnants of this chemistry is hard to say. There is at least some evidence of it in the spectra of comets, and fragments from these continue to form part of the meteoroidal infall. These particles, unless associated with larger meteorites, would be unrecognizable after traversing the earth's atmosphere; they are among the possible treasures to be found buried in protected crevices on the moon.

Light traversing the interstellar smoke has been found to be polarized. If primitive aggregation plays some role in furnishing precursors for biological evolution, this polarization furnishes at least one bias for a decision between levo- and dextro- isomers.

At any rate, possible sources of probiotic nutrition no longer pose a problem. Before the appearance of voracious organisms, organic compounds would accumulate until they reached equilibrium with thermal and radiative decomposition, from which the oceans would furnish ample protection. Locally, the concentration of the soup would be augmented by selective evaporation, and by adsorption onto other minerals. The main gap in the theory, not yet bridged by any experiment, is the actual formation of a *replicating* polymer in such a morass. We are beginning to visualize the essential conditions for chemical replication, and its ultimate realization is foreshadowed both by biochemical studies of nucleic acids and by industrial syntheses of stereospecific polymers.

There is some controversy over whether nucleic acids were the first genes, partly because they are so complex, partly because their perfection hints at an interval of chemical evolution rather than one master stroke. The advantage of the nucleic acid hypothesis is that no other self-replicating polymers have so far been found. But, as an alternative speculation, a simplified protein might replicate by the complementary attachment of acidic versus basic units, perhaps the crudest possible method of assembly. The nucleic acids would be perfections on this theme for replication. The existent proteins do not replicate; with their variety of amino acids, they would have evolved as better adaptations for assuming specific shapes. A comparative view of independent evolutionary systems may at least serve to check such speculations.

Although many steps in the generation of living molecules remain to be re-created, we can state this as a relevant problem for exobiological study, with considerable optimism for the prevalence of life elsewhere. But a sterile planet, too, would be of extraordinary interest to biology for the insight it should give on the actual progress of probiotic chemical evolution.

Natural and Artificial Panspermia

In the foregoing discussion it was tacitly assumed that the evolution of planetary life was a local phenomenon, independent of the incidence of life elsewhere. But, at a time when *de novo* generation seemed less plausible than it does now, Arrhenius defended another hypothesis: *panspermia*, the migration of spores through space from one planet to another. The credibility of the panspermia hypothesis has been eroded mainly for two reasons: (i) the lack of a plausible natural mechanism for impelling a spore-bearing particle out of the gravitational field of a planet as large as the earth, or any planet large enough to sustain a significant atmosphere, and (ii) the vulnerability of such a particle to destruction by solar radiation. In any case, the panspermia hypothesis could be disparaged for evading the fundamental problem by transposing it to an unknown; perhaps scientifically unknowable, site. These difficulties have impeached the standing of panspermia as an experimentally useful hypothesis, but not its immense significance for cosmic biology. In its defense, it might be indicated that, in view of the dormancy of microorganisms in high vacuum and at low temperatures and of their relatively low cross section for ionizing radiations, the hazards of exposure to space may have been exaggerated. The chief hazard to microorganisms might come from solar ultraviolet radiation and the proton wind, but a thin layer of overlying material would shield a spore from these. For the impulsion of particles we might possibly appeal to impacts with other heliocentric bodies, be they grazing meteorites or planetoids in cataclysmic encounters—suggestions not more remote than those invoked for other astronomical phenomena. Nor can we be sure that all the electrokinetic mechanisms which Arrhenius may have had in mind can be excluded from applying to any single particle. In testing for panspermia, we would be concerned first of all for evidence of interplanetary transport of any material. The moon suggests itself as a nearby trap for particles of terrestrial origin, among which living spores or biochemical fragments of them, might be the most characteristic markers. At one spore per kilogram of sample (a weight ratio of 10^{-15}, the sensitivity of easy biological detection would partly compensate for the vulnerability of spores to physical hazards.

The development of rocket-impelled spacecraft has, of course, furnished a mechanism for producing artificial panspermia. Several authors have recently revived Haldane's passing suggestion that life might even have been disseminated by intelligent beings from other stellar systems. That another century of productive science and technology could give the human species this capability would be hard to dispute. The hypothesis is connected with the age or agelessness of the universe, and until we have a basis for decision on this point, and can make independent tests for intelligent life elsewhere, it must join natural panspermia in the limbo of irrefutable, untestable scientific hypotheses. The technique for attempted radio communication with nearby stars has been detailed recently by Cocconi and Morrison.

These new tools for the exploration of the universe have caught many of us unawares, and few can pretend to have recaptured their equilibrium in dealing with these concepts. Irrefutable notions have little scientific values unless they lead to attempts at verification. A priori arguments for the presence or absence of intelligent life on the planets or in nearby stellar systems are equally unconvincing. The skepticism of most scientists is justified not by conviction but by the consistency of negative evidence in the limited scientific data that have so far been collected.

Planetary Targets

The suitability for life of the accessible bodies of the solar system has already received ample attention. Mars is, of course, the likeliest target, most nearly resembling the habitat of the earth. The indicated scarcity of free moisture and oxygen would severely limit the habitability of Mars by man or most terrestrial animals. However, there seems little doubt that many simpler, earthly organisms could thrive there. Indeed, many students have concluded that Mars does have a biota of its own. The most pertinent evidence is perhaps the infrared reflection spectrum recorded by Sinton which indicates an accumulation of hydrocarbonaceous materials in the dark areas. This is complemented by Dollfus' report on the seasonal changes of granularity of these areas. The main reservation that must be registered is that there might be meteorological phenomena involving masses of material which may be carbonaceous but not necessarily living. Most such material on the earth's surface is associated with life. However, this may be connected with the greedy utilization of such compounds by organisms rather than their production by vital synthesis. However, the most plausible explanation of the astronomical data is that Mars is a life-bearing planet. (The term *vegetation* is often used; this should be discouraged if it implies that the Martian biota will necessarily fall into the taxonomic divisions that we know on earth.)

The habitability of Venus is connected with its temperature, a highly controversial subject. Perhaps the most useful first contribution to the exobiology of Venus would be a definitive measurement of its temperature profile. Even should the surface be unbearably hot, this need not preclude a more temperate layer at another level.

The exposure of the moon's surface to solar radiation and the absence of a significant atmosphere have led scientists to discount the possibility of a lunar biology. However, the composition of the moon's deeper layers, below even a few meters be-neath the surface, is very much an open question particularly in the light of Kozyrev's recent reports of gaseous emissions. Realistic plans for the biological study of the moon probably must await the results of chemical analyses. Apart from the remote possibility of indigenous life, the moon is a gravitational trap for meteoroidal material. We may eventually be able to screen large quantities of this virgin material for what Haldane called astroplankton, in an empirical test of the panspermia hypothesis. While exposed deposits would be subject to solar degradation, shaded refuges must also exist. Mercury may be analogous to the moon, except insofar as its dark side may furnish an even more reliable, though much more remote, refuge of this kind.

It may be academic to discuss the exploration of the major planets, in view of their distance and the difficulty of deceleration in the Jovian field. However, their wealth of light elements, subject to solar irradiation at temperatures and in gravitational fields very different from the earth's, offers the most exciting prospects for novel biochemical systems.

Experimental Approaches

A realistic view of our limitations requires that our treatment of this topic be one of utmost humility. Useful landings on planetary targets are fraught with difficulties and hazards, and experiments done at a distance must not be overlooked in the excitement of planning for more adventurous missions. Balloon- and satellite- mounted telescopes can tell much about planetary chemistry, and hence biology, and probes to the vicinity of a planet can furnish additional information prior to actual landing.

It is instructive to ask ourselves how we

might diagnose the existence of life on the earth from distant observations. If we may judge from the photographs so far obtained from high-altitude flights, we could hope to detect only large-scale manifestations of organized culture—cities, roads, rockets. This reserve may not give due credit to the possibilities of high-resolution photography and sensitive infrared spectrometry, and reasonable implications from seasonal changes in the color and texture of terrain. However, we may conclude that distant approaches will be invaluable for deriving preliminary chemical information but probably will not be decisive for exobiological inferences. Even if we could more surely decide that the Martian cycle involved living organisms rather than inanimate chemical transformations, we would still have little insight into the intimate biochemical details which are a major objective of exobiological research. On the other hand, a planet could harbor an extensive biota that would defy detection from a distance, like the biota of our own extensive deserts and deep waters.

Microorganisms, for many reasons, are the best prospects on which to concentrate marginal capabilities. They are more likely to flourish in a minimal environment than larger organisms. The microbes must also precede the macrobes in evolutionary sequence, though we must not suppose that present-day bacteria are necessarily very primitive. The earth is well endowed with both kinds of organisms; we can imagine another world with only microbes, but we cannot conceive of one lacking microbes if it bears any form of life at all. Likewise, taking the earth as a whole, we find that large organisms occupy only a small fraction of the surface. However, we can rea-

sonably expect to find evidence of microscopic life in any drop of water, pinch of soil, or gust of wind. Given a limited sample for study, microbiological analysis will certainly give the most reliable evidence for the presence of life anywhere on the planet. By the same odds the greatest diversity of biochemical mechanisms will be represented among the microbiota of a small sample.

Microbiological probes also offer distinct advantages for the collection and analysis of living material. From a single particle, microbes can easily be cultivated within the confines of an experimental device. In this they remain accessible to physiological and chemical experiments that would be extremely cumbersome with larger organisms. (Compare, for example, the automatic instrumentation that would be needed to catch a mouse or an elephant and then to determine its nutritional requirements!). The techniques of cytochemistry already developed for the chemical analysis of microscopic cells and organisms appear to be the most readily adaptable to automation and telemetric recording, an important advantage under the existing pressure of time, talent, and cost. Important issues of policy cannot be decisively settled without factual information on the growth capacity of the microorganisms that might be exchanged among the planets. Accordingly, methodological precedents in terrestrial science for exobiology are most evident in microbial biochemistry. The conceptual aims are equally close to those of biochemical genetics. Needless to say, no other resource or objective of serious biological science can be neglected in the development of an experimental program.

Aside from experimental designs, the

pace of exobiological research may be regulated by advances in vehicular and guidance capabilities and data communication. In the expectation that these will remain in reasonable balance—for static or real time television communication with the planetary probe—the microscope may be the most efficient sensory instrument. The redundancy of a pictorial image would not be altogether wasted: would we put our trust in a one-bit pulse from and efficient black box to answer our queries about the cosmos?

According to this experimental concept, the terminal microscope-Vidicon chain must be supported by three types of development: (i) for collection and transport of the specimen to the aperture of the microscope; (ii) for cytochemical processing of the samples; (iii) for protection of the device against environmental hazards, for appropriate location after landing, and for illumination, focusing, and perhaps preliminary image selection. Detailed studies of these problems are just under way, and the following suggestions are tentative.

The easiest specimens to obtain may be atmospheric dust and samples of surface soil, once the device has been landed. These would be collected on a traveling ribbon of transparent tape which would be thrown out and then rewound into the device. Larger samples, collected by a soil auger, could be subjected to a preliminary concentration of nonmineral components by flotation in a dense liquid. The use of such a tape would simplify the problem of treating the samples with a succession of reagents—for example, specific enzymes and fluorescent stains for the detection of nucleic acids and proteins. Microscopy with ultraviolet light, particularly at 2600 and

2800 angstroms, owing to its selectivity for nucleic acids and proteins, may be the most direct way to distinguish microorganisms from mineral particles. Generally speaking, the microscope can be adapted to many simple analytical procedures whose construction on a larger scale would present formidable problems for automatic technique.

The adaptation of the microscope system to a payload can be undertaken more realistically when laboratory prototypes have been built and tested. For example, we will have to decide between accurate prefocusing of a microscope whose lenses and entry slit are mounted in a rigid structure and continuous control of focus by an optically controlled servo system (an innovation that would be far from useless in the biological laboratory). Fluorescent staining may facilitate automatic discrimination for conservation of radio power; the traveling ribbon can be stopped and the Vidicon-transmitter activated just when a stained object is in view.

These preliminary experiments can indicate some of the general features of the planetary microbiota. The data they furnish will support more intensive studies of the growth characteristics, chemical composition, and enzymatic capabilities of organisms cultivated on a larger scale. The interaction of these organisms with tissue cultures of animal cells can also be considered. From the results of these initial probes we can better deduce how to anticipate the long-range consequences of the intercourse of planetary biota.

Conservation of Natural Resources

A corollary of interplanetary communication is the artificial dissemination of terrestrial life to new habitats. History shows how the exploitation of newly found resources has enriched human experience; equally often we have seen great waste and needless misery follow from the thoughtless spread of disease and other ecological disturbances. The human species has a vital stake in the orderly, careful, and well-reasoned extension of the cosmic frontier; how we react to the adventuresome and perplexing challenges of space flight will be a crucial measure of the maturity of our national consciences and our concern for posterity.

The introduction of microbial life to a previously barren planet, or to one occupied by a less well-adapted form of life, could result in the explosive growth of the implant, with consequences of geochemical scope. With a generation time of 30 minutes and easy dissemination by winds and currents, common bacteria could occupy a nutrient medium the size of the earth in a few days or weeks, being limited only by the exhaustion of available nutrients. It follows that we must *rigorously* exclude terrestrial contaminants from our spacecraft. This stricture must hold until we have acquired the factual information from which we can assess with assurance the detrimental effects of free traffic and determine whether these are small enough to warrant the relaxation of these controls.

At the present time, the values that would most obviously be threatened by contamination are scientific ones. The overgrowth of terrestrial bacteria on Mars would destroy an inestimably valuable opportunity for understanding our own living nature. Even if an intemperate mission has not contaminated a planet, the threat of its having done so will confuse later studies, if

earth-like organisms are found. However, other values are also involved. Quite apart from strictly scientific concerns, would we not deplore a heedless intrusion on other life systems? It would be rash to predict too narrowly the ways in which undisturbed planetary surfaces, their indigenous organisms, or their molecular resources may ultimately serve human needs. If we have cause to prejudice these values, we surely would not wish to do so by inadvertence.

To guard effectively against contamination requires a nice appreciation of the ubiquity and durability of bacterial spores, which are well preserved in high vacua and at low temperatures and are rapidly destroyed only when kept at temperatures over 160° C. It is probable that spacecraft can be disinfected by the conscientious application of gaseous disinfectants, especially ethylene oxide, but this will succeed only if the procedure is carried out meticulously and with controlled tests of its effectiveness. Sealed components, if found to be potential sources of contamination, can be disinfected by chemicals prior to sealing, or subsequently by heat, or by irradiation at very high doses. The technology of disinfection is an expert one, and personnel already experienced in it should be delegated supervisory control.

The assessment of this problem involves a concept of risk that has not always been perceptively realized. The hazards of space flight itself, or of hard impact, or the planetary environment *might* suffice to neutralize any contaminants, but can we afford to rely on uncertain suppositions when the stakes are so high, and when we have practical means at hand for conservative protection? We must be especially sensitive to the extreme variations in the environments of spacecraft or of planetary surfaces which might furnish refuges for microbe survival no matter how hostile the *average* conditions.

The indication by agencies both in the United States and the U.S.S.R. that adequate precautions will be exercised on all relevant missions is an important step in the realization of constructive exobiology.

Scientists everywhere will call for the application of these measures with the same care and enthusiasm as the more positive, exciting, and patently rewarding aspects of space research. Scientific microbiology in the laboratory is absolutely dependent on the rigorous application of the special technique of pure culture with aseptic control. If we do not exercise the same rigor in space science, we might as well save ourselves the trouble of thinking about, and planning for, exobiological research.

While early traffic to the planets will be one-way, we must anticipate roundtrip, and even manned, space flight. Undoubtedly, planetary samples can be analyzed for any scientific purpose more conveniently and more exactly in the terrestrial laboratory than by remote devices. For each step of analysis, special devices can be used (or if need be, newly designed and constructed), and a constant give-and-take between human judgment and instrumental datum is possible. However, the return of such samples to the earth exposes *us* to a hazard of contamination by foreign organisms. Since we are not yet quite certain of the existence of planetary (that is, Martian) organisms, and know nothing of their properties, it is extremely difficult to assess the risk of the event. The most dramatic hazard would be the introduction of a new disease, imperiling human health. What we know of the biology of infection makes this an extremely unlikely possibility; most disease-producing organisms must evolve very elaborate adaptations to enable them to resist the active defenses of the human body, to attack our cells, and to pass from one person to another. That a microorganism should have evolved such a capacity in the absence of experience with human hosts or similar organisms seems quite unlikely. However, a converse argument can also be made, that we have evolved our specific defenses against terrestrial bacteria and that we might be less capable of coping with organisms that lack the proteins and carbohydrates by which they could be recognized as foreign. Furthermore, a few diseases are already known (for example, psittacosis, botulism, aspergillosis) whose involvement of man seems to be a biological accident. These arguments can only be resolved by more explicit data. Nonetheless, if they are harmful at all, exobiota are more likely to be weeds than parasites, to act on our agriculture and the general comfort of our environment, and to be pervasive nuisances than acute aggressors. However, even the remotest risk of pandemic disease, and the greater likelihood of serious economic nuisance, must dictate a stringent embargo on the premature return of planetary samples, or of craft that might inadvertently carry them. Again, our preliminary experiments must give us the foundation of knowledge to cope with exoorganisms, even to select those which may be of economic benefit. A parallel development of techniques for disinfection may mitigate some of these problems; at present the prospects for treating a returning vehicle to neutralize any possible hazard are marginal by comparison with the immensity of the risks.

Of the possible payloads for interplanetary travel, living man, of course, excites the widest popular interest. In due course, he may be supported by a sufficient payload to accomplish useful tasks in exploration beyond the capacities of instrumentation. However, he is a teeming reservoir of microbial contamination, the most difficult of all payloads to neutralize, and he is an especially suitable vehicle for infectious organisms.

In view of these difficulties and insofar as manned space flight is predicated on the return of the crew, a sound basis of scientific knowledge from instrumented experiments is a *sine qua non* for the planning of such missions.

Timely efforts now to devise and build instrumented experiments is essential to keep pace with the technical capacities of space vehicles.

Conclusion

Many of the ideas presented in this article are not new. In the scientific literature they have been treated only occasionally, for example in a remarkable article by J. B. S. Haldane (1954). They are also anticipated in the classic works of science fiction —for example, H. G. Wells' *War of the Worlds*—and in a flood of derivative fantasies of less certain quality either as science or as fiction. This kind of attention has not necessarily contributed to realistic evaluation of the biological aspects of space travel, discussion of which may still be dismissed as overimaginative by some of our colleagues. However, exobiology is no more fantastic than the realization of space travel itself, and we have a grave responsibility to explore its implications for science and for human welfare with our best scientific insights and knowledge.

XVI

INTERPLANETARY CONTAMINATION, so chillingly fictionalized by H. G. Wells in *The War of the Worlds* in 1898, becomes a distinct possibility as man rockets to other planets. There is real danger that technological advances in space research may outrun biological ones.

In the following article, P. H. A. Sneath divides contaminants into chemical and biological ones. The former are briefly mentioned, but it is the latter that are of chief concern. A single microorganism would suffice in theory to infect a planet. The possibility of contaminating the earth with exobiota from other planets is but one of the problems discussed here. The other problem is our contaminating other planets with terrestrial organisms and thereby confusing the interpretation of data we might find there.

Mr. Sneath speculates on the various kinds of exobiota that might contaminate our planet and the technical problems of disinfection. As he points out, our greatest danger lies not in the technical difficulties, but in apathy. We have now reached the point where the pure culture techniques of Robert Koch must be expanded to cosmic scale.

Dangers of Contamination of Planets and the Earth

From P. H. A. Sneath, "Dangers of Contamination of Planets and the Earth" in *The Biology of Space Travel* by N. W. Pirie (London: Institute of Biology, 1961), pp. 95-105. Reprinted by permission of the Institute of Biology.

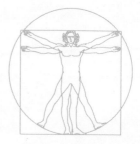

UNTIL VERY recently there has been little awareness of the magnitude of the problem of interplanetary contamination. Many books on Space travel do not mention it, and Tingey[1] notes the lack of comment on a provocative leading article published recently in the *British Medical Journal.* Yet, as has been pointed out by Lederberg[2,3] our knowledge of biology, unlike our knowledge of physics, is confined to the Earth;[4,5] there has been very little development of theoretical biology (again in contrast to the position in the physical sciences) and this is due in large measure to our ignorance of the possible forms which life might take outside our own planet. It would therefore be a scientific catastrophe if we carelessly contaminated another planet and thereby deprived ourselves of the opportunity of studying its indigenous life, or of tracing the evolutionary origin of the creatures which we may find. The problem of the origin of life is one of the greatest challenges of the age, and by blundering, we may prevent ourselves from answering it.

Our objection to interplanetary contamination turns also on a keener edge. If we do not know what we may do to organisms of other planets, neither do we know what they may do to us. We have little reason for complacency. There is a danger that technological advances in space research may outrun biological ones. We may better appreciate these dangers if we consider what would have been the effects of radioactivity in Victorian times if atomic energy had been discovered before the work of Darwin and Mendel and before the development of modern pathology. Yet in both cases there seems to be no reason why the technical advances should necessarily wait on biological science.

We may divide contaminants into chemical and biological. The former are briefly mentioned, but it is the latter which must excite our main attentions. The power of multiplication of living creatures poses difficulties of quite a different order from those raised by chemical contamination. Indeed we may use the ability to multiply as our criterion of life. A single micro-organism would suffice in theory to infect a planet, and in practice very few would be needed if suitable conditions were present for their growth. The standard of decontamination of space vehicles must therefore be very high. We cannot at present exclude the possibility that conditions for the growth of micro-organisms may exist on Mars or Venus or even below the surface of the Moon.[6,7,8] Because of the hazards of contaminating the Earth with exobiota we must also plan to carry out biological experiments on these by remote control on space probes, and microscopic examination of planetary micro-organisms seems entirely feasible.[4,5]

The Dangers of Contamination

"*Scientific microbiology in the laboratory is absolutely dependent on the rigorous application of the special technique of pure culture with aseptic control. If we do not exercise the same rigor in space science we might as well save ourselves the trouble of thinking about and planning for exobiological research*".[4]

The dangers of interplanetary contamination are of two kinds, which are not sharply separable: (1) the loss of scientific information (2) dangers to the ecology of the Earth itself. The loss of scientific information might be enormous. If we contaminate the Moon with terrestrial organisms we may be unable to decide whether any life which we may later find there was the product of an indigenous evolution, or whether they had come (as Arrhenius suggested in his panspermia hypothesis) by migration through space from another planet. The dust on the Moon, particularly where protected from solar radiation, would afford important evidence on this, and even if the terrestrial contaminants were unable to multiply, their presence would still confuse the interpretation of the data.[6,7,8] If the contaminants should multiply, as they might well do on Mars or Venus, the ecology of these planets might be greatly disturbed; not only would there be a danger of extinction of any indigenous organisms, but the terrestrial organisms might metabolize any stores of non-living organic matter, leading to rapid changes in the surface chemistry of the planets. It seems very probable that some terrestrial bacteria could multiply under conditions which occur on Mars;[9] and Kooistra, Mitchell and Strughold and Davis and Fulton have produced evidence in favour of this possibility.[10,11] Some bacteria can multiply in water containing only small traces of nutrients which might well be produced on planets by photochemical action.[12]

"*We have learned now that we cannot regard this planet as being fenced in and a secure abiding-place for Man: we can never anticipate the unseen good or evil that may come upon us suddenly out of space*".[12]

We can make no rational estimate of the dangers to the Earth of contamination by exobiota, since we lack precisely the wide biological theory which we need to do so. They range from the trivial to the threat of extermination of terrestrial life. It is very probable that organisms which have evolved on another planet would be quite unsuited to life on Earth. Yet we cannot be sure of this. Wherever a sizeable geographical area has been cut off from the rest of the world and has then come again into ecological contact there has always been disturbance due to the invasion of new organisms. Many examples of this are well known: for example the rapid spread of the rabbit and the prickly-pear in Australia, the bramble in New Zealand, the Colorado beetle and *Phylloxera* in Europe, the cornborer and the fluted scale insect in America. The destruction of European and Australian rabbits by the myxoma virus is a vivid recent example. Although many of these are pests of a single agricultural crop, this is not always the case. It is of course true that only a small minority of introduced forms establish themselves, and still fewer become pests.

Unfortunately our poor theoretical background of biology does not afford us many clues of what to expect of organisms of a different evolutionary history and possibly of a different chemical constitution. We may dismiss the remote possibility that any form of life which flourishes at temperatures over 100°C or below 0°C (such as silicon-based organisms or those with liquid ammonia as internal solvent, mentioned by Haldane or the stellar dust-cloud biota imagined by Hoyle in his novel *The Black Cloud*[13,14] could become established on the Earth. We may also here leave out of account the sentient monsters of science fiction. The most likely exobiota would be carbon-based, though possibly they would utilize elements which terrestrial organisms do not.[15] If their constitution were based on the same polymers as terrestrial organisms, i.e. nucleic acids and proteins, they could probably multiply on Earth. If they were based on other polymers this would be less certain, but they might possess powers of assimilation and digestion which terrestrial organisms could not resist. Precisely the opposite argument could also be advanced— that they would themselves be destroyed by terrestrial organisms. Whether terrestrial organisms could develop immunity to the tissue constituents of exobiota is another difficult question.

The Earth may be susceptible to damage in many unsuspected ways. Apart from the obvious dangers of pandemics of disease of man or his animals and crops, there are less obvious dangers which could be equally ruinous. J. J. Connington in his novel *Nordenholt's Million* tells the story of the failure of agriculture due to a denitrifying bacillus.[16] Any organism which made unavailable such soil constituents as phosphates, manganese, or iron would be equally disastrous.[17] Lederberg points out that there are a number of diseases in which the causative organism appears to derive no benefit from its pathogenicity, and in which the ill-effects seem to be an accidental side-product of their growth. [4] Botulism is one of the best examples, and one might add others like tetanus, the intoxications caused by dinoflagellates, the blue-green alga *Microcystis*, poisonous coral fishes, and, perhaps such infections as melioidosis and chromobacteriosis.[18,19] It is therefore possible that exobiota might produce metabolites which were by accident highly toxic to some terrestrial organisms, and if they affected agricultural plants this might be a serious matter. It is possible that together with the evolution of resistance to microbial infection the higher organisms have also developed resistance to the antibiotics produced so commonly by micro-organisms; such resistance may not protect against antibiotics of exobiota. Nor should we lose sight of the possibility that relatively simple polymers might be able to replicate and cause virus-like diseases.

The problem of contamination by chemical substances which do not multiply is much smaller. There is little likelihood that any significant amounts of toxic or radioactive material would be accidentally introduced into planets by space vehicles. Such compounds could still prove troublesome on small bodies such as the Moon, for the low gravitational field would allow them to spread widely from the point of impact if they were dispersed on landing. Any material, such as radioactive elements, which could be a source of confusion for subsequent scientific exploration should be excluded as far as possible from space vehicles. There would be an advantage in employing where possible characteristic materials which were stable and unlikely to occur naturally, such as the fluorocarbon plastics. The detection of chemical contaminants is much less sensitive than that of biological contaminants; Lederberg estimates that a single viable spore could be detected in a kilogram of dust—a ratio of 1 in 10^{15}.[4]

Resistance and Longevity of Organisms

We are much better informed of the resistance of terrestrial organisms to inimical agencies than we are of the limits of their longevity in a state of dormancy. All known organisms are killed in a few minutes by moist steam at $130°C$, by powerful oxidizing agents and by heavy doses of ionizing radiation. When perfectly dry, for instance when freeze dried *in vacuo*, they may resist any temperature below that at which charring begins to occur. It seems likely that in many cases it is the extensive breaking of carbon-carbon bonds which is responsible for the loss of vitality.

We know much less about the longevity of organisms. The excellent review of Keilin summarizes most of our knowledge.[20] The longest periods of survival of bacteria which I have been able to find are the records of viable spores in canned meat after 113 years and of anthrax spores prepared by Louis Pasteur which were viable after 66 years.[21,22] I have recently found high counts of viable bacilli (almost all were spore forming bacilli) in soil from the roots of pressed and dried plants from the Kew herbarium which were over a century old. The counts were much higher than can readily be accounted for by recent contamination, and the data suggest a 'half-life' of about 20 years for spores of certain species of *Bacillus*. It is well known that many non-sporing bacteria will survive for twenty or thirty years if dried *in vacuo*. Meyers and Griffith reported that pony droppings from Scott's Antarctic Expedition of 1911 still contained viable coliform bacteria after being continuously frozen for nearly fifty years.[23] Over 1,000 viable coliform bacilli per gram were found in this material by Professor R. H. McBee (personal communication). I have not been able to trace any work on the microflora of the frozen mammoths of Siberia, though this must have aroused interest. There is evidence that some plant seeds can survive for over a century, and in one case, the seeds of the lotus *Nulembo nucifera*, for 800 to 1,200 years.[20]

At very low temperatures, such as may occur in space and in crevices on the Moon and other planets, the length of survival is probably much greater than any mentioned above. Becquerel has argued that at temperatures close to absolute zero micro-organisms would survive for thousands of millions of years. [24,25] We should also not lose sight of the possibility that the simpler viruses (and also polymers such as nucleic acids) may survive without inactivation for far longer than other organisms. Their ultimate death, and that of organisms at very low temperatures, may be largely a consequence of the accumulated dosage of ionizing radiation (in protected material mainly cosmic rays and natural radioactivity), though over a few thousand years this would probably have no significant effect. It is often assumed that organisms could not survive in space because of the intense solar radiation. Sagan has calculated that unprotected spores would be rapidly killed, but even light protection would allow prolonged survival.[8] The very short ultraviolet rays would be stopped by very thin films of material, while a covering, a few centimetres thick, would protect against all but the more penetrating radiation of X-rays and high energy cosmic rays. Any micro-organisms within a space vehicle would therefore be protected, and the panspermia hypothesis cannot be entirely ruled out since micro-organisms embedded in meteorites (originating from a glancing collision of a meteor and a planet) would be able to survive for long periods, and even some higher organisms might also do so.[26]

We can only guess at the resistance of exobiota. If we confine ourselves to carbon-based life we may expect that disinfection procedures which cause disruption of carbon-carbon bonds would be adequate. But if the exobiota have high resistance to desiccation and ultraviolet light (as might well be true of organisms which have evolved in the harsh climates of other worlds) this will raise a second problem, that of the rapidity of their spread over the whole earth. It is clear that atmospheric carriage (and also water-borne carriage) of micro-organisms around the world is swift: the reason terrestrial micro-organisms do not spread so readily is because they do not survive during transit. Even on this point our knowledge is not very full, and it would be instructive to study the spread of organisms chosen for their natural resistance, such as the micrococci which are so common in air samples.

Technical Problems of Disinfection

We still know little of how heavily machinery and similar equipment is contaminated with micro-organisms, and how we may best sterilize them. It is clear from the report of Fabian and Pivnick that bacteria may be abundant in oils used in machining.[27] Because of their high vacuum, radio valves may be ideal for preserving the viability of bacteria which become incorporated during manufacture. Recently Davies and Comuntzis have described the difficulties of sterilization of space vehicles.[28] Many components cannot be heated to 160°, as would be desirable. Ethylene oxide was suitable for sterilizing most components. Yet other components must be sterilized by pentrating gamma radiation. Higher organisms would be much the most heavily contaminated of all the contents, and would present a much greater problem.

A casing must be fitted onto the rocket for the launching to prevent its outer surface picking up contamination and the casing can be released when the vehicle enters outer space. It is abundantly clear that much more work will be needed in this field.

When we turn to the problem of disinfecting material from another planet we are hampered by our ignorance of the degree of resistance to heat, radiation or chemicals which exobiota may possess. We cannot assume that even powerful chemical disinfectants will prove effective, or will penetrate impervious protective coats, and non-penetrating radiation will be ineffective. The only safe rule will be to heat the samples to temperatures above 160° so that they begin to char. This implies that we dare not attempt to study such exobiota on the earth, even "dead" ones, until we have much experience of their properties.

It is likely that the progress in space technology will present us successively with the problems of the contamination of the planets, of space stations and of the Earth, and we may briefly consider some technical problems of these in turn.

The contamination of planets could be avoided by proper sterilization of our space probes, at least until we were prepared to make manned landings. When this does happen we hope to have much more knowledge of the dangers, but clearly we will wish to use a careful system of disinfection in the air locks of space vehicles, both to prevent contamination of the planet and to protect the personnel against exobiota. Heat-resistant materials for space suits, etc. will be invaluable in this connection. If, as Parkes and Smith mention, we should wish to carry out a colossal experiment in evolu-

tion on a planet by introducing terrestrial organisms we shall certainly wish to keep our experiment under the strictest control.[26]

The sterilization of space vehicles has been considered above. Their decontamination, should they become contaminated with exobiota, may be less easy. It may be difficult at first to recognize the contamination. If need be the vehicle could be abandoned by its personnel and then be destroyed, either by directing it into the sun or by vaporizing it in a small nuclear explosion.

If contamination was accidentally introduced into the earth the technical problems would be very great. All the health and agricultural services of the world should be alerted. If the returning vehicle crashed a large area might be biologically contaminated, and this would require all the ingenuity we have, for unlike chemical contamination, we would have to try to ensure that not even a single organism escaped destruction. An immediate precaution would be to cover the site with plastic sheeting to prevent windborne spread or washing into the soil by rain. If the sheet was weighted down by intense radiation sources this would sterilize the top few centimetres of soil in which most of the contamination would be. Decontamination on rocket sites on ice would be easiest, since surface melting, radiation, chemical disinfection and heating of the water from the melted ice should together give complete decontamination. The ice below would presumably be impervious to seepage. There would be some danger of overlooking contamination which might remain dormant for long periods. Desert sands would be more difficult to handle. The sand could be flooded with hot oils or self-setting resins, and then excavated and burnt. In such circumstances even the use of a nuclear explosion might be considered, though there might be a risk of spreading such contamination as escaped the heat and radiation, or of driving it deep into the ground. Moist earth on porous rock would be exceedingly difficult to decontaminate, since seepage into the subsoil would be rapid.

Planning of Experiments on Space Stations

There can be no excuse for introducing organisms to earth or to planets in the early stage of space biology. It is equally undesirable to try to grow planetary organisms in terrestrial laboratories or terrestrial micro-organisms in planetary ones. The latter alternative indeed is almost unnecessary since we can grow terrestrial organisms on Earth in chambers made to mimic the conditions of planetary surfaces (though technical problems, e.g. the imitation of the dust of Mars, might tempt us to the very dangerous practice of bringing such dust to Earth for these experiments).

The only safe and practical method would be to carry out all the early and critical experiments on space stations. The advance in remote control mechanisms and the use of the isolating property of empty space would allow such experiments to be made in earth satellites. At the conclusion of the work the experiment chamber could be disinfected or destroyed. Some of the critical experiments will be those in which a small ecological structure was inoculated with planetary material. For example, it might consist of terrestrial soil with grass, insects, rodents and agricultural plants, in a sealed chamber, under artificial gravity and illuminated by artificial light. Other systems would be marine pools, peat moss and desert scrub, and would include higher animals, wood, fabrics, metals, etc. in order to detect destructive action on both non-living and living material. If no ill effects could be observed after prolonged study of several such systems we would feel more confident that unwelcome microexobionts were not common, and might with greater safety allow the study of planetary materials under sealed conditions on the Earth. Vigilance would still be needed, since dangerous exobiota might exist but might be rare. In space stations, too, we could extend the experiments on exobiota which had been started in unmanned vehicles as Lederberg has suggested. [4,5]

Science Fiction and the Biologist

We may legitimately allow ourselves the relaxation of reviewing what writers of popular science fiction have imagined on the subject of inter-planetary contamination. Although most of their suggestions seem of vanishingly small probability, yet by a happy chance one or other may be near the truth; their imagination may stand us in good stead of our own by suggesting possibilities which we had never entertained.

For much of these comments I am indebted to the brief but convenient history by Moore.[29] Space travel had been envisaged by Lucian (fl. A.D. 150), but the first writer to propound the theme of the "threat to Earth" was H. G. Wells, in his classic novel *The War of the Worlds* (1898). This threat took the form of what were also the first hostile intelligent beings in science fiction (affectionately known to the craft as Bug-Eyed Monsters, or B.E.M.s for short). They projected themselves from Mars to the

Earth by rocket, and, armed with a heat ray (the first of the "Death Rays") attempted to colonize the earth. To this was added the unprepossessing trait of using man as food. Every reader of this book will recall that they were defeated by terrestrial bacteria. Mars, said Wells, had no micro-organisms and the Martians had therefore no immunity against even the most harmless of terrestrial saprophytes, and soon died. The same fate overtook the "red weed", a prolific plant which had been introduced from Mars. While we may not think it plausible that a planet should possess intelligent beings but no micro-organisms, and although Wells proposed almost the reverse of the situation which we fear, nevertheless he introduced the powerful idea that what are simple and harmless creatures could, in the context of space biology, become the most potent of weapons. "By the toll of a billion deaths, man has bought the birthright of the earth". But not, we may add, the birthright of other planets. The superlative imagination of this book may be judged from the fact that Wells also anticipates automatic machines which copy themselves and describes in the Martians the super-specialization of the brain as compared to the rest of the body. It is also the only work of science fiction which has caused a serious panic—a radio production which shook New England on 31 October, 1938 —although we may perhaps allow that the producer, Orson Welles, had a hand in this.

Other cosmic threats in science fiction have ranged from the production of deformities and mutations by deadly radiations (John Taine in *The Iron Star*) to ichneumonism (*The Voyage of the Space Beagle* by Van Vogt) and cuckooism (John Wyndham, *The Midwich Cuckoos*). One of the most plausible stories is *Nordenholt's Million* by J. J. Connington, referred to above. In this a bacterium of great denitrifying activity, the *Bacterium diazotans* of uncertain provenance, converts the combined nitrogen of the soil to nitrogen gas with consequent breakdown of soil structure as in "dust bowls", and the world-wide failure of agriculture.

In conclusion we may note that there is a growing realization of the dangers of interplanetary contamination, see for instance the CETEX report[30] and several papers read at the 10th International Astronautical Congress and the 1st International Space Science Symposium. The Russian lunar rocket "Lunik 2", which hit the moon, was sterilized, and American space probes have been similarly decontaminated. Our greatest danger lies, not in the technical difficulties, but in apathy. But if we blunder carelessly on I do not know just what future biologists can forsee for Man.

References

[1]Tingey, A. J. C. 1960. "Space Travel". *Brit. med. J.*, 1, 504.

[2]Anonymous. 1959. "Keep the Planets Clean". *Brit. med. J.*, 2, 811-812.

[3]Brown, J. R. 1960. "Space Travel". *Brit. med. J.*, 1, 730.

[4]Lederberg, J. 1960a. "Exobiology—approaches to life beyond the Earth." *Science*, 132 n.s., 393-400.

[5]_____ 1960b. "The search for life beyond the Earth". *New Scientist*, 7, 386-388.

[6]Lederberg, J., and Cowie, D. 1958 "Moondust". *Science* 127 n.s., 1473-1475.

[7]Sagan, C. 1960a. "Indigenous Organic Matter on the Moon". *Proc. nat. Acad. Sci., Wash.*, 46, 393-396.

[8]_____ 1960b. "Biological Contamination of the Moon". *Proc. nat. Acad. Sci., Wash.*, 46, 396-402.

[9]Sinton, W. M. 1959. "Further Evidence of Vegetation on Mars". *Science*, 130 n.s., 1234-1237.

[10]Kooistra, J.A. Jr., Mitchell, R. B., and Strughold,

H. 1958. "The behaviour of micro-organisms under simulated Martian environmental conditions". *Publ. astr. Soc. Pacif.*, 70, 64-69.

[11]Davis, I., and Fulton, J. D. 1959. "The Reactions of Terrestrial Microorganisms to Simulated Martian Conditions". *Proc. 10th International Astronautical Congress*, London, pp. 778-785, Vienna, Springer.

[12]Garvie, E. I. 1955. "The Growth of *Escherichia coli* in Buffer Substrate and Distilled Water". *J. Bact.*, 69, 393-393.

[13]Haldane, J. B. S. 1954. "The origins of life" in *New Biology* No. 16, pp. 12-27. Harmondsworth: Penguin Books, (135 pp.).

[14]Hoyle, F. 1957. *The Black Cloud*. London: Heinemann. ($\times$ + 251 pp.).

[15]Pirie, N. W. 1957. "Chemical diversity and the origins of life", in *The Origin of Life on the Earth, Reports on the International Symposium, August,* 1957, *Moscow*, pp. 55-61. Moscow: U.S. S.R. Academy of Sciences (391 pp. illust.).

[16]Connington, J. J. (penname of A. W. Stewart). 1923. *Nordenholt's Million*. Reprinted in 1946, Harmondsworth: Penguin Books, (286 pp.).

[17]Needham, A. E. 1959. "The Origination of Life". *Quart. Rev. Biol.*, 34, 189-209.

[18]Bishop, C. T., Anet, E.F.L.J., and Gorham, P. R. 1959. "Isolation and identification of the fast-death factor in *Microcystis aeruginosa* NRC-1". *Canad. J. Biochem. Physiol.*, 37, 453-471.

[19]Sneath, P. H. A. 1960. "A Study of the bacterial genus *Chromobacterium*". *Iowa St. Coll. J. Sci.*, 34, 243-500.

[20]Keilin, D. 1959. "The problem of anabiosis or latent life: history and current concept". *Proc. roy. Soc. B.*, 150, 149-191.

[21]Wilson, G. S. & Shipp, H. L. 1938. "The Exami-nation of Some Tinned Foods of Historic Interest. Part 4. Bacteriological Investigations." *J. Soc. chem. Indust.*, 57 *(Chem. Indust.,* 16), 834-836.

[22]Jacotot, H., and Virat, B. 1954. "La longévité des spores de *B. anthracis* (premier vaccine de Pasteur)". *Ann. Inst. Pasteur,* 87, 215-217.

[23]Meyers, C. E., and Griffith, P. M. 1959. "Sources and isolation of micro-organisms from Antarctic specimens". Paper read to the Society of American Bacteriologists, Northern California and Hawaii Branch, April, 1959.

[24]Becquerel, P. 1950a. "La vie latente des graines aux confines de zéro absolu". *C. R. Acad. Sci., Paris,* 231, 1274-1277.

[25]_____ 1950b. "La suspension de la vie des spores des Bactéries et des Moisissures desséchées dans le vide, vers le zéro absolu. Ses conséquences pour la dissémination et la conservation de la vie dans l'Univers". *C.R. Acad. Sci., Paris,* 231, 1274-1277.

[26]Parkes, A. S., and Smith, A. U. 1959. "Transport of life in the frozen or dried state". *Brit. med. J.*, 1, 1295-1297.

[27]Fabian, F. W., and Pivnick, H. 1953. "Growth of Bacteria in Soluble Oil Emulsions". *Applied Microboil,* 1, 199-203.

[28]Davies, R. W., and Comuntzis, M. G. 1959. "The Sterilization of Space Vehicles to Prevent Extraterrestrial Biological Contamination". *Proc. 10th International Astronautical Congress, London,* pp. 495-504, Vienna, Springer.

[29]Moore, P. 1957. *Science and Fiction*. London, Harrap, (192 pp.).

[30]CETEX Report. 1959. "Report of the Committee on the Exploration of Extra-terrestrial Space". *Nature Lond.,* 183, 925-928.

F OR DECADES astronomers have observed that the Martian spring is
heralded by the appearance of a green belt near the equator of that
planet. Of the theories advanced to explain this phenomenon, perhaps
the most intriguing is that which proposes the presence of plant life.

If human beings get to Mars or Venus, will they find vegetation?
Will it be suitable for sustenance? Could life, as we know it, exist on
those planets? Could humans adapt to these new environments?

In the following article, Hubertus Strughold, often called the father
of space medicine, summons persuasive evidence to answer each of
these questions.

On the Possibility of Life under Extraterrestrial Conditions

From Hubertus Strughold, "Physiological Considerations on the Possibility of Life under Extraterrestrial Conditions" in *Space Medicine*, edited by John P. Marbarger (Urbana, Ill.: The University of Illinois Press, 1951), pp. 31-47. Reprinted by permission of the publisher.

THE QUESTION of whether or not life is possible outside the earth—for instance, on other celestial bodies—has kept the minds of men preoccupied for centuries. Due to the lack of necessary scientific foundation, most considerations have ended in the vagueness of imagination. Today this is quite different. During the first half of this century important discoveries have been made by physicists studying the higher atmosphere, the stratosphere, and ionosphere, and by astronomers in planetary research. During the same period of time, physiology and aviation medicine have made remarkable progress in the study of the stages and limits of life. In fact, progress in these fields has reached a stage which permits a serious scientific discussion on the possibility of life outside the earth. Today, the modern devel-opment of rockets, which makes it possible to reach the border zone between atmosphere and space, will add new findings by way of experimentation and, with each further step advancing into space, will give renewed impetus to the study of the problem of extraterrestrial life.

Life, as we know it, can exist only under certain environmental conditions. These include temperature, light, and substances required for growth and energy production. The most important of these so-called bio-elements are oxygen, carbon, nitrogen, and hydrogen. These factors set limits to life either if they are too strong and abundant or too weak and sparse. A certain minimum must be reached and a certain maximum must not be exceeded; only within these limits, life can develop. In the geographical distribution on earth of man, animals, and plants, we observe limits set by temperature, humidity, sunshine, by the chemical composition of the soil, the water, and the air. Between these two cardinal points of the *maximum* and the *minimum* lies the *optimum* of an environmental condition or of a combination of such conditions, which is particularly favorable for life to flourish. Naturally, these three cardinal points are not fixed but vary with the different types of organisms. In short, the *law of optima* and the *law of minima* (Von Liebig) or the *principle of the limiting factors* (Blackman), both of great importance in the ecology and economy on earth, afford the best clues as to the problem of life on other planets.

In the following, therefore, I will discuss some of the aforementioned environmental factors under the aspect of these principles. I am going to limit this discussion to two of these factors, *temperature* and *oxygen*.

Let us presuppose, in this discussion, that the physical chemistry of the living processes in the entire universe is the same as that here on earth, and that the chemistry of all living matter is based on the carbon atom.

Let us start with *temperature*. Of the entire temperature range from absolute zero to one billion degrees Kelvin, only a narrow band of about 60° C. permits the existence of life (figure 1). Below this range of bio-temperatures, as I choose to call it, the reaction kinetics of the molecules slow down and finally cease completely. Above this range the molecules soon break up on account of thermal dissociation. Above 3,000° K the atomic shells begin to break up as a result of thermal ionization, and above 10 to 20 million degrees Kelvin the temperature affects even atomic nuclei. The left side of

the diagram of figure 1 shows the temperature ranges of planets and stars.

If we now enlarge the scale of the lower part of figure 1 as in figure 2, we obtain the following picture:

Active phenomena of life, such as metabolism, muscle and nerve activity, reproduction, etc., can take place only within the temperature range of the living matter, between some degrees below the freezing point of water and about 60° C. Only a few types of bacteria are able to withstand temperatures exceeding the boiling point of water. When exposed to extreme cold, most organisms soon die. But there are lower plants, such as bacteria and lichens, which in a form of latent life resist temperatures near absolute zero for weeks.

If we now study the temperatures of the planets, we find that Mercury's temperatures lie far above the maximum cardinal point. Venus, with more than 100° C. in its lower atmospheric layers and about −25° C. in its outermost stratum, approaches biological temperatures only in certain higher strata. The temperatures found on earth, ranging from −60 to 60° C., cover the entire range of active life with its upper half; they also cover 50° C. of the cold range of latent life. The Martian temperature range within its upper quarter coincides with the lower part of the "biothermal band," and covers more than 60 centigrades of the cold range of latent life.

Jupiter with −130° C., Saturn with −150° C., Uranus with −170° C., and Neptune and Pluto with roughly −200° C., are past all hope for active life. Their temperatures lie deep in the cold temperature range of latent life.

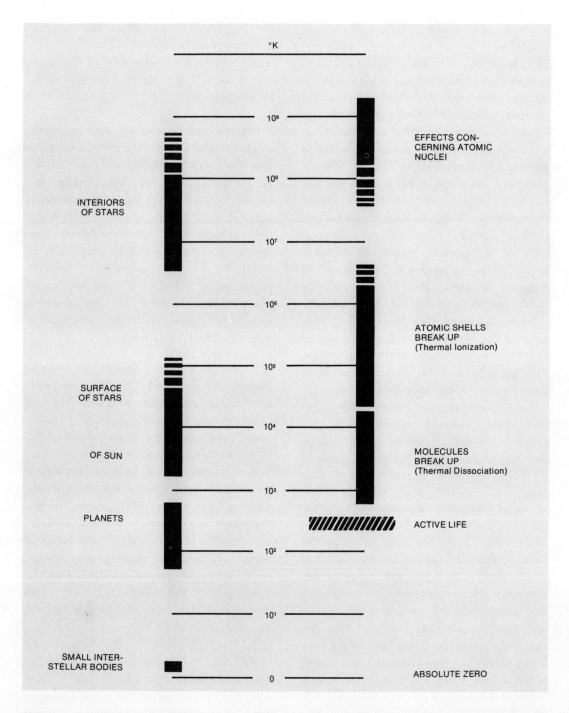

Figure 1 *The known temperature range, showing narrow temperature span in which active life can exist.*

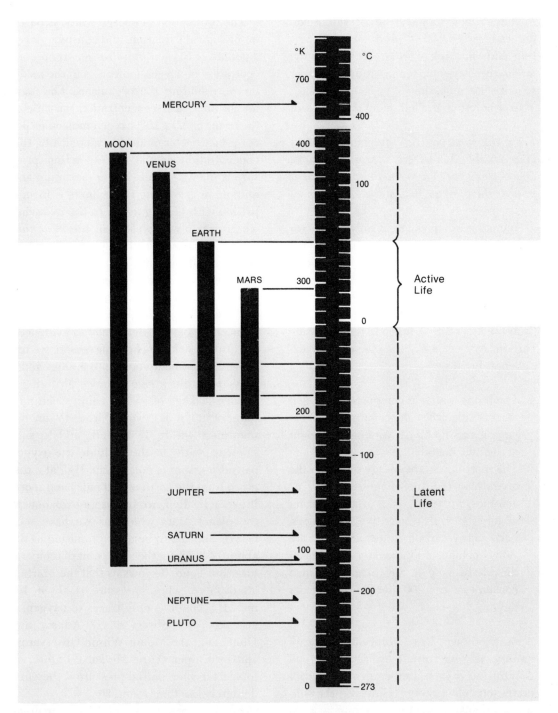

Figure 2 *Lower portion of Figure 1 in detail, showing temperature range of the planets and the bio-thermal band.*

The surface temperature of the moon ranges between 100° C. and −150° C. Setting aside the lack of an atmosphere on the moon, these extreme temperature peaks per se make life impossible.

In conclusion, the following may be said:

From the standpoint of temperature, Mars and possibly Venus are the only planets, apart from the earth, which at present possess the prerequisites of life in our sense.

Temperature, however, is only one factor —though the most important one—in the combination of environmental conditions. Another decisive factor is *oxygen*. At the time of its discovery a hundred and fifty years ago, oxygen was already called the "substance of life." Indeed, setting aside carbon, oxygen is *the* bio-element par excellence, because:

1. The living matter is composed of oxygen to a considerable extent; for instance, oxygen makes up 60 per cent of the weight of the human body.
2. The most important energy source of the organisms, the biological oxidation or aerobic respiration, is a process during which the body's nutritive substances, particularly carbohydrates and fats, are slowly combusted into water and carbon dioxide by oxygen. For this process man consumes about 500 liters of oxygen per day.

Another, though less significant, source of energy is anaerobic respiration which requires no oxygen and, consequently, liberates much less energy. However, the substances that undergo this process consist in a rather large part of oxygen.

The production of energy which is based on biological oxidation, and consumes large amounts of oxygen, requires a certain concentration of oxygen molecules in the medium surrounding the organisms. For man, for instance, this concentration must be of the order of 5.5 x 10^{18} oxygen molecules per cubic centimeter of air. Physiologically, this concentration or the corresponding pressure is likewise limited by a maximum and minimum; exceeding these limits is incompatible with life (figure 3). In the following we are mainly interested in the *minimum oxygen pressure* which is just sufficient to permit a "vita minima."

For man the minimum oxygen pressure is about 65 mm. Hg. However, below 100 mm. Hg. our efficiency and vitality are already reduced by oxygen deficiency as evidenced by altitude sickness. For this reason, we use oxygen equipment above 2 to 3 miles and a pressure cabin above 7 miles altitude. A sudden leakage of such a cabin at an altitude of 20 miles would lead to unconsciousness within 13 seconds and to subsequent death. At this altitude the oxygen partial pressure is only 2 mm. Hg.; at a distance from the earth of 100 miles and more, it is practically zero. Let us go back now to the planet Mars which, as we have seen before, appears to be most promising as the abode of life from the viewpoint of temperature. But figure 3 shows us that the Martian atmosphere, whose pressure is about 100 mm. Hg. contains only traces of oxygen, if any, as was observed by Adams and Dunham at the Mount Wilson Observatory and by Kuiper at the McDonald Observatory. Its oxygen partial pressure is therefore definitely less than 1 mm. Hg.

In this case then, intelligent manlike creatures do not exist; for the minimum ox-

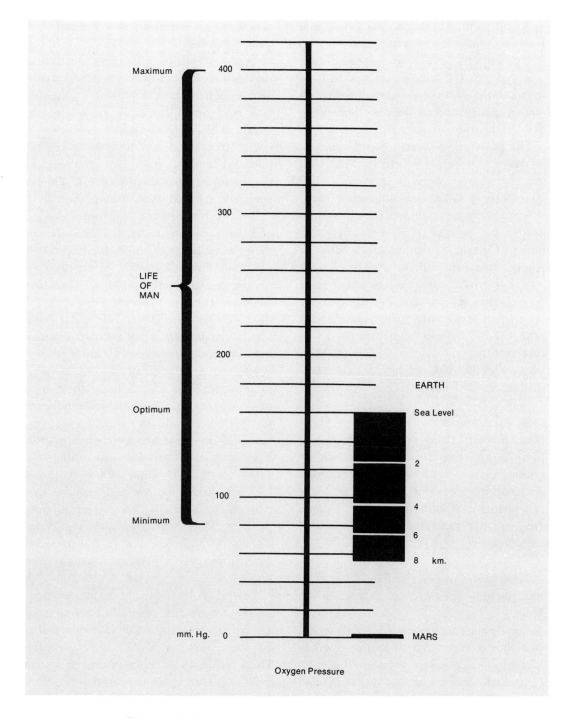

Figure 3 *Limits of oxygen pressure compatible with human life.*

ygen partial pressure required by man is at least 100 times the pressure existing on Mars. Martians, who—as was repeatedly announced over the radio—were said to have invaded the earth and caused casualties among panic-stricken people, belong indeed to the realm of fantasy.

The presence of homoiothermic animals on Mars must be precluded, for their vital minimum oxygen pressure is hardly below 50 mm. Hg. Poikilothermic animals, however, such as frogs, fish, crabs, etc., can endure oxygen pressures of 10 to 1 mm. Hg. for hours. Certain lower species, such as worms, can live without oxygen. Yet, it would be absurd to speculate about their possible presence on Mars. Perhaps one can say that, if at all, only lower animals with little need of oxygen (and little need and content of water) are able to live on Mars because of the planet's low temperatures (and scarcity of water).

In short, *from the standpoint of vital oxygen pressure, man and animals except those of the very lowest species can be excluded from life on Mars with certainty. Any positive arguments as to the presence of lower animals with little need of oxygen are and will remain speculations for lack of any clues.*

There are, however, visible clues as to the possible presence of *vegetation* on Mars.

For decades astronomers have observed that during each Martian spring, a green belt appears around the region of the equator which later becomes yellowish and brown (figure 4). In other words, Mars shows seasonal changes in color as they are commonly known in vegetation. From these manifestations recurring each Martian year, quite a number of astronomers inferred the presence of plants. Others assumed that these manifestations are caused by varying degrees of hydration of minerals on the surface, and one astronomer spoke, for instance, of blooming crystals.

But let us suppose that there is vegetation. What then, from the physiological standpoint can we say, in view of the *oxygen lack* in the Martian atmosphere?

It is true that plants also show respiration and that they require oxygen, even though they can switch to an anaerobic respiration any time. For full growth, plants need an oxygen pressure certainly higher than that on Mars. There is, however, one faculty of the plants which in this respect makes them superior to animals. They not only consume but also produce oxygen. This latter process is effected, as is generally known, by *photosynthesis*. The plants have their own oxygen generators in the chlorophyll-containing chloroplasts. In daylight a leaf surface of 25 m.^{2} produces as much oxygen as is consumed by an adult man during the same period of time. Photosynthesis requires carbon dioxide and water as raw material, as well as light and a certain temperature. How are the environmental conditions on Mars in view of this process? Well, they are in part moderate, in part poor.

First of all, the temperature minimum for photosynthesis lies generally some degrees around the freezing point of water. But it has been reported that it starts in some kinds of lichens at temperatures as low as −20° C. During a summer day on Mars these temperatures are exceeded by 20° C. to 40° C. according to W. W. Coplentz and C. O. Lampland.

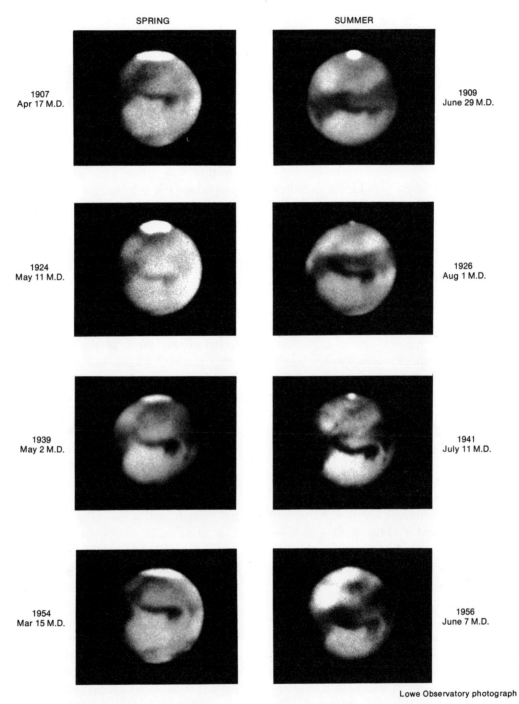

Lowe Observatory photograph

Figure 4 *Photographs of Mars in different seasons, showing the gradual melting of the snow cap and intensification of the dark blue-green areas (Martian dates).*

Second, the intensity of solar radiation amounts to about 40 per cent of that on earth.

Third, the carbon dioxide amount in the Martian atmosphere is, according to Kuiper even somewhat higher than that on earth.

Fourth, the presence of water may be taken for granted; yet as compared with the Earth, Mars must be considered a very dry planet.

If the latter factor should not definitely and constantly be below the minimum, photosynthesis on Mars might be possible in view of the adequacy of all the other factors. It is, however, most unlikely that plants of higher order, such as vascular plants, can exist on this planet. Only very resistant dry plants, so-called xerophytes, could withstand such extreme climatic conditions. In this respect, certain hints were obtained by Kuiper's recent observations at the McDonald Observatory. He found that the infrared reflection spectrum of the green Martian regions is incompatible with that of the higher green plants on earth, but not with that of lichens and moss. Lichens and moss belong to the two lowest subdivisions in the plant kingdom, the thallophytes and bryophytes. The lichens, especially, show particular features. As is well known, they consist of two dissimilar organisms, a fungus and algae living in symbiosis. The fungal component supplies inorganic material and protects the algae from drying out. The algal component, in general the *Protococcus viridis,* builds up organic substances by photosynthesis and produces oxygen. On account of this ideal symbiosis, lichens are very resistant to a dry and cold environment, and have hardly any demands as to the kind of substratum upon which they live. Thus we find them growing

on barks of trees, or even on the surface of rocks, etc. In the subarctic tundras they represent the great majority of vegetation.

In the Himalayan mountains they can be found at altitudes as high as 15,000 feet. In short, they are the "last outposts" of plant life in every direction. They can exist on bare rocks because of their ability to decompose rock by producing organic acids. In this way, they are "pioneer plants," preparing the humus for the more demanding plants. In the course of the earth's history they may well have made the first start for vegetation that has developed in sterile volcanic regions. This phenomenon can be observed, for instance, on the huge lava masses of the Sunset Crater in Arizona.

Might it not be possible that the lichens, as pioneer plants and last outposts of vegetation on our earth, play a similar role on other planets? Might similar plants not be the last outposts of vegetation in the planetary system as well, on Mars for instance, even though there is no oxygen? For better understanding let us look at the microscopic anatomical side of these questions.

In figure 5 you see the thallus of a foliose lichen in cross section. It shows an upper and a lower compact layer of dense mycelial threads, and a looser layer in between. The algal cells are scattered below the upper layer. The looser middle layer contains large air spaces. For our discussion the air spaces are most significant. Air spaces combined with pores within the epidermis have developed also in higher plants. Especially pronounced are the air spaces in the leaves of water plants.

A principal fact is that the atmosphere proper, through which the cells effect their gas exchange, is found within the leaf, in the intercellular air spaces. It is the *system*

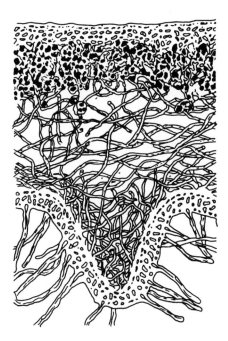

Figure 5 *Cross-section through the thallus of the lichen* Lobaria pulmonaria. *After Weise from Tobler.*

of air spaces (aerenchyma) from which the cells of the parenchyma draw carbon dioxide and where the oxygen required for respiration can be stored. Consequently, the cells are not in direct contact with the ambient air (external atmosphere) but only with a "private" atmosphere which they supply themselves (internal atmosphere).

The famous French physiologist Claude Bernard created the terms *milieu intérieur* and *milieu extérieur,* meaning interior environment and exterior environment. The former is the physicochemical milieu in the cells themselves and in the body fluids of an organism; the latter stands for the physicochemical milieu of the surroundings. The example of the plants, however, shows that still another milieu may be interposed. The principle of an intermediate milieu, as we may call it, permits the existence of plants

in an oxygen-poor or oxygen-free *milieu extérieur.* Water plants give a good example of this situation. Might it not be possible that the development on Mars runs along similar lines?

In this case, then, the oxygen problem of the Martian plants is solved, even if there is no oxygen in the atmosphere. The only difference between Martian and terrestrial plants would be that the latter have the advantage of drawing oxygen continuously from a reservoir of 1.2 billion tons, whereas Martian plants get their oxygen only from "current production." They consume the oxygen *in statu nascendi,* or take it from the small stores of the microclimate within themselves.

In conclusion we may say: If the green areas on Mars should actually be vegetation, and if the plants should develop along the lines we have outlined just now, then we must assume that these plants show active life only during the day, as soon as the combination of environmental conditions exceeds the effective threshold for photosynthesis; during the cold night, however, they would return to a latent or dormant state. The active life of Martian plants would thus be intermittent. Perhaps on our earth, during the Proterozoic era 800 million years ago, the first primitive life was also intermittent.

The last drawing (figure 6) shows the stages of vegetation on Mars and on earth, as may be assumed from the combination of environmental conditions present on these two planets. The vegetation on Mars—if there is any—can, at the most, be of the tundra variety, spreading over a narrow belt. In contrast, the earth shows a plant kingdom of profuse abundance. Of all planets, the earth appears to be blessed

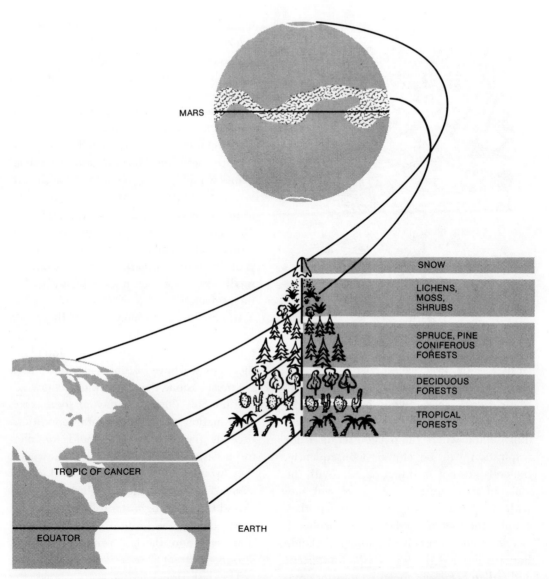

MARS

SNOW

LICHENS,
MOSS,
SHRUBS

SPRUCE, PINE
CONIFEROUS
FORESTS

DECIDUOUS
FORESTS

TROPICAL
FORESTS

TROPIC OF CANCER

EARTH

EQUATOR

Figure 6 *An assumed comparison of vegetation on Mars and the earth.*

with a combination of conditions best suited for the development of life; it has the best place under the sun. It is the biocenter of our solar system. Looking at it from this aspect we might say that Ptolemy was right.

Now one might ask, why such studies about extraterrestrial life? The answer is this: Comparative planetary biology affords new and attractive aspects for terrestrial physiology, biology, and palaeobiology. Furthermore, if some day rockets should open the gates to space, then we must be orientated as to its environmental conditions and their possible biological effects. To study this, and to find means of protection, is one of the tasks of space medicine.

Not only is victualling in space not an immediate problem, it will not even become a theoretically interesting one for between 10 and 100 years." So wrote N. W. Pirie in 1961 in the following article. Now, with the breathtaking advances in space technology in the intervening years, we might well assume that the problem has become one of at least theoretical interest.

Almost all aspects of life in space ships are considered here by Mr. Pirie—from the problem of boredom to cosmic gardening—and the reader picks up much fascinating information along the way from the fields of biochemistry, biology and physiology.

Besides the wealth of information he presents, Mr. Pirie also includes some provocative judgments. He concludes that space travel is not likely to be useful; that is to say, it will not ameliorate the lot of the ordinary person. He feels it is "monstrous that useless research should become a major preoccupation while there are people with empty bellies in the British Commonwealth and drab old women pushing wheelbarrows in the mud of Moscow building sites."

Most interesting of all, perhaps, is Pirie's conclusion that there are probably organisms elsewhere far more highly developed than we are, and that if they have not come here, it is unreasonable to think that we will be able to get there.

The Maintenance of Life in Space Ships

From N. W. Pirie, "The Maintenance of Life in Space Ships—
Synthesis, Recycling, and the Steps Towards a Microcosm," *The
Biology of Space Travel* (London: Institute of Biology, 1961),
pp. 21-31. Reprinted by permission of the Institute of Biology.

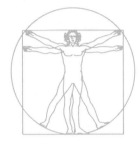

ARISTOPHANES, the father of space travel,
did not describe the food taken by Trygaeos on his flight to heaven, but he showed
his usual perspicacity by choosing a dung
beetle as the vehicle. With that steed, he
pointed out, it would only be necessary to
carry new food for one. Clearly, our
problem has a respectable antiquity and
more recent writers have been remiss in
skating round it with casual references to
sandwiches or, like Hans Pfaal, pemmican.

Before victualling an expedition we must
decide how long it is going to last—that is to
say "Where is it going?" and "At what
speed?" The questions are interdependent.
Until much greater speeds than the present
half million miles a day are attainable, it is
safe to assume that people will not get very
far—and get back. If only one-way trips are
contemplated the problems become simpler
but different. Arbitrarily we may take 10 M
miles a day as a reasonable speed and this,
as the troubles with rockets using conventional fuels as a source of power show, will
only become possible when nuclear reactions provide the drive. An improvement in
performance is needed similar to the one
that has taken place between the original
invention of rockets by the Chinese and the
present day. That sets a time scale; the sort
of rocket that can be taken seriously as a
means of space travel will not soon be
made. Not only is victualling in space not
an immediate problem, it will not even
become a theoretically interesting one for
between 10 and 100 years. Table 1 shows
that the minimum distance from Earth to
Venus is 26 M miles and from Earth to Mars

49 M miles. The times-of-flight for a round trip will not be six and ten days respectively for, as every student of the popular articles on possible satellite orbits knows, it is necessary to follow a more circuitous course. But, even if the space ship has to chase Venus or Mars half way round the solar system, the flight will last months rather than years. That then is the scale of the problem that will first be posed.

To be properly fed a sedentary person needs 2,500 kilo calories a day and the main foods—protein, fat and carbohydrate—supply respectively 4.1, 9.3, and 3.8 k cal. per gram. With conventional foods therefore the daily consumption of dry matter will be about 400 g, depending on the subject's tolerance for fat, and no form of concentration or substitution of new synthetic foods will diminish this significantly so long as the body is fuelled by eating. Some alternatives to eating will be considered later. A 70 kg astronaut would therefore take six months to eat his own weight of dry food. That would allow reasonable nutrition and would maintain body weight. Space travel will involve so many hazards and inconveniences, ranging from collision with meteorites to loss of body weight, that a considerable loss of body mass is unlikely to be looked on as fundamentally objectionable so that that ration could be stretched to last for about a year. In the less prosperous parts of the world many are living on less food than that and the literature of human misery, from shipwrecks to Belsen, shows what privations we can stand and still act and think effectively.

Destination	Distance from the Sun in million miles	$\dfrac{\text{Distance of Sun}^2}{\text{Distance of Earth from Sun}^2}$	Relative intensity of sunlight
Mercury	36	0.15	6.7
Venus	67	0.52	1.9
Earth	93	1	1
Mars	142	2·3	0.45
Jupiter	483	27	0.03
Saturn	886	91	0.01
Uranus	1783	370	0.003
Neptune	2793	910	0.001
Pluto	3660	1560	0.0006

Water, quantitatively, is a bigger problem than food. We lose on the average 0.8 litres litres a day by evaporation from lungs and skin when sedentary and have to pass 0.4 through the kidneys to keep them in good order. Some of this water is made by the oxidation of hydrogen in our food. The total need is therefore a litre a day and this quantity is less subject to variation than the food intake. The need for water is so large, and it matters so little from a physiological stand-point where it comes from, that we can dismiss as nonsense much that has been written about the space traveller eating compressed pills. He has to get his water from somewhere and might as well get some of it from moist foods with the accustomed texture rather than drinking it all. The only advantage in having food dry, so that it actually weighed the theoretical 400 g a day, would be that it would keep better. With modern packaging techniques this advantage loses significance.

Finally there is oxygen. If the astronaut is not increasing in weight most of the 400 g of food a day reappears as CO_2, H_2O and urea and this combustion uses about 1 kg of O_2. The amount of O_2 needed depends on the ratio of fat to carbohydrate. If it is high the demand for O_2 increases because carbohydrates contain, from this point of view, solidified oxygen. In semi-starvation the O_2 demand will remain near its normal value, because it is needed to burn the tissues lost during emaciation. As with water there is little flexibility in this demand.

In total therefore, between 2 and 2.5 kg of material has to be provided every day. With the necessary containers that would amount to well over a ton for each person if the vehicle started with a full complement of provisions for a year's flight. All of this material is converted into the various excreta. Something has to be done with them. They could be jettisoned and, once drive was shut off, accompany the traveller through space as Jules Verne's dog did. It is tempting to think of recycling, with the space ship operating as a closed system so far as matter is concerned, and driven by a suitable energy supply.

Some recycling will be forced automatically on the traveller. Thus most of the water drunk re-appears as water vapour and will condense on any cold part of the ship. It would be necessary in any event to localize the condensation by having an uninsulated panel radiating heat into space, and what is condensed would be potable. The recovery of most of the water in urine also presents few difficulties. With abundant energy a simple still would suffice and only a little more weight would be introduced if a more elaborate still were used that made use of the astronaut's own body heat. His daily calorie output is ten times what would be needed. Complete recovery of water is unnecessary; if exhaled water and most of the water in urine were recovered the daily demand for new water could be reduced to about 200 g.

Similarly something must be done with exhaled CO_2 and this will not be so easy. It is unlikely to prove practicable to condense CO_2 out and jettison it although, with ample external cold on the dark side of the ship, the prospects are a little better than they would be on Earth. If it were absorbed by an alkali, the carbonate could be jettisoned. In practice a peroxide would be used; with KO_2 each molecule of CO_2 liberates more than one of O_2 so that this would cope with diets containing a large proportion of fat and so giving Respiratory Quotients less than one. Ideally, assuming again that energy is abundant, the CO_2 should undergo a dismutation to O_2 and free carbon or carbon in unoxidized combination. Some such recovery process will be essential on long journeys, so it deserves a little attention even although there will be great difficulties in bringing the actions about with light equipment in a confined space. In theory it should be possible to make C or CH_4 from CO_2 electrically for this is simply the mechanism of the fuel cell run in reverse. The C, or CH_4, would be jettisoned and the process would be worth carrying out because, in the ratio of 44 to 12, it is better to jettison C than CO_2.

It would be better to make something of use to the astronaut. The problem is: what? Various enzyme processes are known that use CO_2 to lengthen carbon chains and make substances such as oxaloacetic and malic acids. As they stand these actions would not go far towards solving the problem, for 80-90% of one's C excretion is in the form of CO_2 and it is unlikely that even 1/10 of one's calorie intake could be met by these acids. They might however be used as starting materials for chemical syntheses. From the standpoint of space travel a person's needs are inconveniently diverse but not infinitely so. We need a dozen trace elements and a dozen vitamins, but a year's supply of them only weighs a few grams. The dozen amino acids, one or two fats and some sources of energy are the serious problems. Some of these could, in principle, be resynthesized now and it is reasonable to think that, in the course of one or two decades, more will be, but the methods we think of now are useless for the purpose because they do not depend on energy sources that can reasonably be postulated as continuously available in the ship. The solution generally advocated is to reconstruct in space a process such as we use on Earth and have organisms or groups of organisms, that can make from CO_2 a range of substances as diverse as we need, and eat the organisms. As if Trygaeos had finally eaten his dung bettle.

There has been much recent popular writing on cosmic gardening with transparent cells or tubes, on the surface of the space ship, in which algae or some other photosynthetic organism would reconvert CO_2 into edible protein, fat and carbohydrate which could be eaten. There are obviously great possibilities here and the diet should be nutritious and need not be unappetizing; leaf protein is a similar product and it is palatable.[1] But the advocates of this approach often seem not to have heard of the "inverse square law" and sometimes not even to have been out at night. The paramount fact about space is that it is dark; our judgement gets warped because we happen to live in one of the illuminated enclaves in it. But the blackness of the night sky shows how trivial they are. Table 1 shows the relative intensities of sunlight on the different planets. Clearly all is well as far as Mars but the illumination near Jupiter is only just above the compensation point, that is the brightness at which a plant absorbs CO_2 by photosynthesis more rapidly than it makes it by respiration. For journeys beyond Mars photosynthesis dependent on sunlight need not be taken seriously in spite of science fiction writers.

There has been much controversy about the maximum rate of photosynthesis and about the relative merits of higher plants and algae for bulk production of human food. Under normal circumstances the higher plants appear to be preferable because of the simplicity of their cultural requirements,[2] but conditions will be different in a space ship and a suspension of algae or photosynthetic bacteria has obvious advantages over a plant with leaves and roots. A square meter of culture exposed to sunlight as far out as the orbit of Mars should fix 100 g of CO_2 in 24 hours; at this rate, 5 to 10 square metres of photosynthetic surface would be needed to cope with the breath of one person. The surface of the smallest vessel in which it would be practical to keep a person for a prolonged period would therefore be adequate to maintain a respiration cycle so long as the traveller does not get more than about 200 M miles from the Sun.

This is not the place to go into details of the design of an interplanetary greenhouse, but a few points are necessary for the development of the argument. For adequate light absorption a layer of algal culture 1-2 cm deep would have to be circulated through cells or tubes with a double or triple transparent skin for heat insulation. The pump and gas exchange system, in which O_2 is liberated and CO_2 absorbed will, together with the illuminated part, hold about 200 kg of suspension. And the equipment itself would weigh the same or more. Some of this weight would naturally be in place of and not in addition to the normal mechanical, insulating and micro-meteorite-stopping, shells of the ship, but it is not unreasonable to think that the photosynthetic system needed to maintain one person as part of a closed cycle would weigh half a ton. In principle the algal suspension would be fed with urine and the nitrogen from that, together with the carbon from the CO_2 absorbed, would be returned as algal substance. This might well satisfy half of the astronaut's food requirements. For long journeys some such arrangement has obvious advantages. But its advantage within the illuminated zone of the solar system needs careful quantitative analysis. No one is likely to go circling round the Sun except through inadvertence. Journeys are likely to be purposeful and to follow the shortest course so that, if my earlier premiss is accepted that no journeys are likely to be undertaken at all until propulsive units able to give speeds of about 10 M miles a day are available, the times we are concerned with are of the order of 100 days. For flights of that duration it seems as likely that stored nutrients and jettisoned excreta will give the answer.

Having reached this borderland between science fact and science fiction, it may be permissible to speculate. The simplest means of ensuring that an astronaut will be functional after a long interval without raising the metabolic problems that have been discussed so far, would be some form of anabiosis. This was the means used, in H. G. Wells fantasy, to cope with temporarily superfluous labour on the Moon. Keilin has carefully reviewed the serious literature of the subject from Leeuwenhoek to the present day.[3] Anabiosis, or cryptobiosis as Keilin suggests it should be called, may seem improbable in man whether achieved by cooling as John Hunter suggested, or drying, as in lung fish or in the story "L'homme á l'oreille cassée" published by E. F. V. About in 1862, but it seems the only manner in which the problem of boredom will be overcome during journeys outside the solar system. Cryptobiosis is however an evasion rather than a solution of the problems with which this paper is concerned.

Seeking other solutions to the problems of maintaining life in a metabolically active person who is not growing, we may consider some conceivable alternatives to eating. Intravenous injection of metabolites and other forms of parenteral feeding might help a little by reducing digestive work and wear and tear on the gastrointestinal tract but the effect would probably not be great. More is to be hoped for from the reversal of metabolic processes by the application of an external source of energy. So far there are only hints of the directions in which this might be possible. For example, Abbott and Bigland find that, if two bicycles are connected in such a way that work done by one person pedalling forwards is absorbed by another person backpedalling, less work is done by the latter.[4] They suggest that this happens because muscles used to resist work rather than to do it can partly reverse their metabolic cycles. Also, there is some evidence that electricity applied across the stomach wall can be used to supply part of the energy needed to make HC1.[5] This is a tenuous basis for speculation. Nevertheless, when we consider the changes that have come over our biochemical outlook and capabilities in the last few decades, it seems not improbable that, after a similar interval, it may be possible to do much of the work of the body by the application of external energy sources, or to use such sources to regenerate metabolites that have been used.

A very interesting feature of modern biochemistry is the constant appearance of the same intermediate molecules—adenosine triphosphate, flavine adenine dinucleotide and triphosphopyridine nucleotide—in different reactions. Much of the metabolic work of the cell is concerned simply with restoring these substances to the effective state of phosphorylation or reduction that they lose when bringing about an action. This is a job that should be possible by external means. If these intermediates were in serum it could be done with a dialysis system along the lines of an artificial kidney; to restore them inside the cell will not be so easy but, remembering the time scale with which we are concerned, it should be possible. Another possibility arises if Karreman and Steele are correct in thinking that it is no accident that so many components of biochemical systems are coloured and that some of the energy in a cell is transferred by resonance.[6] If so, radiation should be a possible means of introducing the energy needed to reactivate intermediates. And finally, among these speculative possibilities, Armstrong and Szent-Gyorgyi have suggested that a protein fibre is an energy-transferring system along which electrons can flow as they do in a semiconductor.[7, 8, 9] On this view, simple contact with a suitable generator should suffice to recharge the enzymes in a system. The vagueness of these suggestions illustrates how little we know of the physics of energy transfer in and between cells but they clearly make it conceivable that it will at some time be possible to "plug in" the astronaut to the electrical supply of the ship and so diminish his need for food.

Developments along the same lines may be possible with autotrophic organisms of types that can be eaten. An autotroph uses an energy flux to convert simple carbon and nitrogen sources into protein and the other substances of which it is made. For example, the use of light to reduce CO_2 is the primary overall reaction of a green plant. This reaction is the basis of life on Earth, its role in scavenging the space ship while it is near the Sun has been discussed, and it is obviously possible that it could also be used in the dark parts of space. To achieve this, an artificial light source would be needed. For this approach to be useful in a space ship the source of energy must be lighter and more compact than the normal fuels for these offer no advantages over stored food that is large enough to compensate for the weight of equipment needed to bring about the recycling reactions. In effect this again brings us to the necessity of a nuclear power unit. But even when that is available there will be difficulties.

At rest, a person uses about 100 watts. If food equivalent to that amount of metabolic energy is to be the product of a series of inefficient conversions from nuclear energy, through electricity and light, to photosynthesis, the input is likely to be about 4 HP. To maintain an equilibrium, in this microcosm, between photosynthesis with an artificial light source, and the astronaut's metabolism, it will be necessary to dissipate the surplus energy from these inefficient processes as heat; this in the near vacuum of space, will not be easy. Given time it should be possible to make the process more efficient. But light is not the only form in which energy can be fed into an autotrophic system; it has become dominant on Earth only because it is the main energy flux that exists here naturally. Some autotrophs depend on a valency change, e.g. the conversion of ferrous iron to ferric, for their energy, and this suggests the possibility that electrical energy could be used to drive the endergonic reactions of the organism. This could be done either directly, or by having a separate vessel in which ferric iron is reduced to the ferrous state, with liberation of O_2. This mode of approach to the problem seems more probable than the one proposed in the previous paragraph, for much selection and breeding will be needed to get organisms amenable to these sophisticated forms of metabolism so that fast-breeding micro-organisms have obvious advantages.

Water, CO_2, and urea are not the only end products of metabolism and, although adequate techniques for recycling these will so diminish the demand for stored food that journeys lasting a year or more should become possible, the minor products will raise problems on more prolonged journeys. Nitrogen metabolism may be used to illustrate the point, though it arises with equal force for sulphur and phosphorus. Nitrogen, whether derived from the daily intake of food or from tissue breakdown during semi-

starvation, appears mainly as urea but 10-15% is in more complex forms of combination in faeces, and 3-4% is in hair, nails and normally abraded skin. During a year that only amounts to 1 kg of N or 6 kg of dry protein; it would therefore be reasonable to jettison it on journeys of that length but on longer journeys it would mount up and would have to be brought back into circulation by either chemical or microbiological processes. This would call for some form of sewage farm. Boredom is often listed as one of the hazards faced by the astronaut; it is possible that the supervision of all the systems needed to keep the metabolic cycles going on a long journey will keep him rather busy.

A very important merit of research along these lines is that it would be generally useful and would be a natural extension of biochemistry—increasing our understanding of how organisms work and increasing the possibilities of improving them or curing them of diseases. At present, Space Research is essentially a diversionary activity. It sucks off into channels that will have little effect on the life of the ordinary citizen a vast amount of money and skill that is badly needed in more useful directions. It is sometimes argued, and I have much sympathy with the argument, that this work should not be considered in terms of ordinary scientific budgeting at all and that it is done for military reasons or for prestige in international politics. If it is done for prestige and if "face" can be gained or saved by sufficiently dramatic exploits in space, it will justify almost any expenditure. So much the better if useful by-products can be made to flow from the expenditure.

To complete the discussion of space victualling the remote possibility of finding suitable nutrients after a landing must be considered. Given suitable thermal and gravitational conditions, water will be present; its presence or absence can therefore be predicted with some certainty for any destination. Predictions about O_2 are very much less certain. Some people maintain that all the atmospheric O_2 was originally made on Earth by photosynthesis, for this is how it is replenished now; this is extremely unlikely. Pre-carboniferous deposits contain vast amounts of sulphate and ferric compounds whereas magmatic materials are in the reduced state. This "fossil oxygen" presumably came from the primitive atmosphere and was made there by the photolysis of water with subsequent loss of H_2 to space. The O_2 pressure in the probiotic atmosphere was however probably low and it would be unreasonable to expect a pressure great enough to support human breathing on any other member of the solar system. But even a few millimeters pressure of O_2 could, with compression and, if necessary, fractionation, be the starting point for making a breathable gas mixture.

Speculation on the nature of any organisms that may be found is active. They are more likely to look familiar than to be familiar. Although it has evolved very slowly, structure depends on certain universal geometrical principles: two or four legs are adequate for motion as soon as sense organs can react to changes in orientation in a time adapted to the local gravitational acceleration, in other circumstances an animal must crawl or use more legs; paired sense organs aid depth perception; a leafy structure is a necessary preliminary to efficient photosynthesis; light absorption must be in a range near the energy maximum for the local source of light; and so on. These considerations make it unlikely that the dominant living forms, if any, on a planet with similar gravity, temperature and light intensity to Earth, will have an appearance totally unlike any of the forms that exist or have existed here. The accidental assorting of qualities may, however, give dominance in one environment to a form that is relatively unimportant in another. Similarity may not go further than superficial structure. Organisms on Earth are the products of a few lines of descent and are now parts of an integrated food cycle; in a strange earthly land a traveller may therefore reasonably expect some of the exotic organisms to be edible. But on a strange planet there is no similar basis for expectation. C H O N P etc., being relatively common elements, may well play a prominent part in any living processes that exist but they may be combined in other ways than are used in the organisms we know. It is customary to warn astronauts of the possibility of organisms using a stereoisomer different from the one used here. The warning should be generalized. Even if protein-like structures are used, they are likely to contain other amino acids in place of some of those we are familiar with. And accidents in the course of evolution may have given prominence to elements that are either unused or unusual in biology here.[10] H. G. Wells foresaw that invaders from Mars would be more vulnerable to the bacteria of Earth than to its weapons; the converse is also probable. A prudent visitor to another planet will approach any organisms there with circumspection; it will be unwise even to get out of the ship let alone start eating any local products until careful tests have been made.

Repeatedly in this article I have said or suggested that victualling a space ship for long voyages is an interesting but not urgent problem. In conclusion some reasons for this unfashionable point of view may be stated.

1. Space travel is not likely to be useful, that is to say, it will not ameliorate the lot of the ordinary person. Glib talk about the usefulness of new born babies and about Columbus should not be allowed to confuse the issue. We know, broadly, the potentialities of babies, and Columbus was making a voyage of the same character as other profitable voyages but in a new direction. There is good justification for expecting advantages to flow from babies and sea voyages but no similar justification with space travel. This is not an argument for having practically useful research only. But it is monstrous that useless research should become a major pre-occupation while there are people with empty bellies in the British Commonwealth and drab old women pushing wheelbarrows in the mud of Moscow building sites.

2. Serious space travel depends on the development of propulsion units with mass/power ratios of a different order from those used now, though these units may be adequate for some scientific survey flights. Better units will take some time to develop.

3. Normal methods of food storage may well prove sufficient for it may never be possible to get outside the solar system. This, defeatist, idea is a logical extension of the revolution started by Copernicus. That moved Earth from its traditional position in the centre of the Universe and made it a satellite of the Sun. Later work makes it probable that there are millions of similar suns and they may have planetary systems similar to ours; the assumption that among all these, Earth is the only one with life on it, or that evolution has proceeded here furthest, depends on the same naive arrogance that Copernicus rescued our forefathers from. It therefore becomes logical to expect, rather than merely to admit as a possibility, that there are organisms elsewhere far more highly developed than we are. If they have not come here, it is unreasonable to think that we will be able to get there. This is not the place to speculate on the types of difficulty that may be met, they smack of science fiction and they have been considered elsewhere,[11] but this consequence of the outlook implicit in the Copernican revolution should be taken seriously.

References

[1] Morrison, J. E. and Pirie, N. W. 1960. "The presentation of leaf protein on the table." *Nutrition*, 14, 7.

[2] Pirie, N. W. 1958. "The use of higher plants for storing solar energy" in *Use of Solar Energy*, Tucson, Arizona 4, 115.

[3] Keilin, D. 1959. "The problem of anabiosis or latent life; History and current concept." *Proc. roy. Soc. (B)*, 150, 149.

[4] Abbott, B. C. and Bigland, B. 1953. "The effects of force and speed changes on the rate of oxygen consumption during negative work. *J. Physiol.*, 120, 319

[5] Crane, E. E. and Davies, R. E. 1951. "Chemical and electrical energy relations for the stomach." *Biochem. J.*, 49, 169.

[6] Karreman G. and Steele, R. H. 1957. "Long-distance energy transfer by resonance in biology." *Biochim. Biophys. Acta*, 25, 280.

[7] Armstrong, H. E. 1904. "Studies on enzyme action. V. Enzyme action as bearing on the validity of the ionic dissociation hypothesis and on the phenomena of vital change." *Proc. roy. Soc.*, 73, 537.

[8] Szent-Gyorgyi, A. V. 1941. "Towards a new Biochemistry?" *Science*, 93, 609.

[9] Szent-Gyorgyi. A. V. 1947. *Muscular Contraction*. New York, Academic Press.

[10] Pirie, N. W. 1959a. "Chemical diversity and the origins of life" in *The Origin of Life on the Earth*, p. 76. London, Pergamon Press.

[11] Pirie, N. W. 1959b. "The method, myth, and mania of space travel." *Envoy*, 4, no. 9.

P ERHAPS THE MOST unchanging element in our society is change. Change is the watchword of modern life. Each day we see new records in speed, efficiency and technical facility.

Now, suggests John R. Platt in the following article, we are reaching a leveling-off period. Most of the dramatic changes that have characterized the twentieth century, like those in travel, communications and weapons, cannot continue at their present rates. Many of them must converge rather soon to various kinds of limits, so that these aspects of society must begin to take on much more stable forms.

Mr. Platt suggests that the slowing down of growth and the beginning of our adjustment to it may become one of the major social phenomena of the next 30 years.

If we can survive the threat of nuclear destruction, and if we can control population growth, then we will have passed through a kind of cultural "shock front," with each type of exponential change reinforcing all the others.

Then it will be possible, Mr. Platt feels, for mankind to become a closely interconnected species, a species in full possession of the world and its abundance. Our knowledge of nature will be used increasingly for the improvement and variation of our biological apparatus. It will be a time when accident and drift will finally begin to be replaced by conscious human values and decisions. "We have, says Mr. Platt, "been men. We are emerging into man."

The Step to Man

CHANGE, change, change, continual change. This is the watchword of modern life. We have not only adjusted to it, many of us have begun to revel in it. Conservative scientists have predicted the end of change at various times, but they have always been proved wrong. It seems it must go on forever. In the last two decades, the changes have been coming faster than ever before. Planes have passed the speed of sound, bombs have become incredible and then incredible squared, men are in orbit; and here below, new countries have proliferated, television has become universal, and every corner of the world is in a state of ferment.

Yet it seems to me that the excitement of our changes and emergencies has led us to look at them on too short a time scale. Let us not view them through the eyes of the newsman with this month's crisis or the advertiser selling this year's cars or even through the eyes of the planner announcing development programs for 15 years ahead. Let us look at our changes under the aspect of history. Grandparents are still alive who saw the coming of the motor car and the airplane.

Let us look at least as far ahead, to the time when our children will be grandparents in the 21st century; or 100 or 500 years ahead of that—to a time, say, as far away as the Renaissance is today.

I think anyone who does this will soon realize that most of the dramatic changes that have characterized the 20th century, like those in travel and communications and weapons, cannot possibly continue at the present rates for anything like these lengths of time. It becomes obvious that many of them must converge rather soon to various kinds of limits, so that these aspects of society must begin to take on much more stable forms.

Should it surprise anyone that there might be an end to structural change in society? A boy does not go on growing forever. He finally reaches manhood and stops —though his mature accomplishments are just beginning. Likewise if a world once becomes unified, by communication and travel and mutual danger, into one world, the situation must level off. What more is there to do in that direction?

Many of our important indices of technical achievement have been shooting up exponentially for many years, very much like the numbers in the biologists' colonies of bacteria, that double in every generation as each cell divides into two again. But such a curve of growth obviously cannot continue indefinitely in any field. The growth of the bacterial colony slows up as it begins to exhaust its nutrient. The exponential curve bends over and flattens out into the more general "S-curve" or "logistic curve" of growth. Stevan Dedijer, of the University of Lund, and Derek DeSolla Price of Yale University, in his book *Little Science, Big Science* (Columbia Univ. Press, New York, 1963), have recently emphasized that research-and-development expenditures in the United States are now slowing up their rate of growth in just this way and are already beginning to be "past the middle of the S-curve." The reason is clear. Big research-and-development depends on big money, and these expenditures are beginning to exhaust their nutrient.

But I think this phenomenon of slowing up is now becoming much more general. Many scientists seem to suppose that we are just at the beginning of a curve of indefinitely accelerating change. They point out that Laplace and then Michelson long ago predicted the end of change in physics and that they were wrong. But it is one thing to see a slowing up of intellectual returns in certain areas, and another thing to see that life is short and the world is small and that there are physical and natural and economic limits to everything. I think it can be shown that many of our present changes are already rushing rapidly toward such limits. And many of our social adjustments to change are well on their way to what might be called "steady-state forms" that could accommodate orders of magnitude of further technical development without much additional restructuring.

I suggest that it is time to consider a different view, that we are not at the beginning of continually accelerating change, but that we are in the middle of a unique transitional crisis, like adolescence, as we make the jump from an undeveloped scientific and technological society to a fully developed one. Who knows?—we may be even beginning to be past the worst of the crisis, at least in countries like the United States. The slowing down of growth and the beginnings of our adjustment to it may become one of the major social phenomena of the next 30 years. Do you doubt this? Take a brisk excursion with me through some of our important areas of change and see if it is not so.

Plateaus in Sciences and Technology

Consider for example what is happening at present in certain technical fields, as typified, say, by the high-energy accelerators of modern physics. DeSolla Price shows in his book that for 35 years now, we have been increasing the energies of our largest accelerators almost exponentially, as Fermi pointed out some years ago. It is worth quoting some of the numbers, although very approximate figures will suffice for the points I want to make. In the late 1920's, atomic particles could be accelerated to roughly 500,000 electron volts of energy. Successive inventions raised the limit to about 20 million electron volts in the 1930's; to 500 million by about 1950; and to 30 billion by the 1960's. Today, one machine under construction is designed for 50 billion electron volts. This is an increase by a factor of 10^5 in energy in these 35 years, or a multiplication of the energy by another factor of 10 in every 7 years.

Can new inventions raise the energies by still another factor of 10^5 in the next 35 years? Perhaps, but many doubt it. The reason is money. At present there is talk of a 200-billion-electron-volt accelerator which will cost far over 100 million dollars; and after that, of a 1000-billion-electron-volt machine. But this would be so large that it might require international cooperation to finance, and the work of thousands of physicists and engineers for 10 years to construct —that is, a major fraction of all the money and effort likely to be spent on physics in the whole world in that period. There are protests from other scientists whose projects are equally in need of money. Loud objections are being heard not only in scientific societies but in the halls of Congress.

Of course this probable leveling-off of one expensive field does not mean that the era of change is over, even in physics. Other areas of exponential progress may appear

again and again. But this example shows us what forms and limits, from now on, will shape them all. Research-and-development is now a major social business, to be planned for, to be encouraged more richly than ever, to be put to immediate use when possible—and to be consciously limited to a fraction of the national resources and the national budget that is probably not far above the 20 billion dollars, or 3 percent, that is presently being spent on it in the United States. There is a plateau here, an organizational steady state, that we have nearly reached already.

Let us go on to consider another rapidly changing technical field and one with more social impact, the field of computing machines. In the last 20 years or so, the 10-place desk calculator has been surpassed first by John von Neumann's ENIAC computer at the end of the war and now by much faster and more sophisticated devices. It is hard to give exact figures for the improvement in speed and capacity of the machines in this period because the principles of operation have changed drastically, but it might be estimated as a factor of roughly 10^5. In one instance that I know of, a brilliant student in the early 1950's took 2 years on a desk computer to do a quantum-mechanical calculation that was done 5 years later on an electronic computer in 14 minutes. By now, the time required to do this calculation, once a machine has been programmed for it, is probably less than 1 minute.

Today the designers of solid-state and other advanced computers say that a further increase in speed and capacity by a factor of 10 or 100 is in sight, but they do not seem to expect another factor of 10^5 in the next 20 years. When the information travels between the parts of a computer with the velocity of light, the natural limit to the speed of operation has been reached, and this is a limit which is no longer very far off.

It is true that we are probably on the verge of great developments in applying computers to pattern perception and learning and to complex manipulating systems. But computers are already an integral part of advanced science and business and government. Machining and accounting and management and strategy problems are increasingly being turned over to them. It is therefore a little hard to see how even a dramatic extension of their powers could make as much further difference to our attitudes and ways of life as their development up to the present level has already made.

This may possibly be true even of the application of computers to automation, which is threatening to give us leisure in the decade ahead. This is sure to produce in the long run a great social restructuring; yet it is a restructuring which is already well under way. The problems produced by the elimination of labor are not the problems of the 30 hours a week, or 10 hours, or none, that a man works. They are problems of coupling this to economic distribution and to self-respect, and problems of idleness and boredom in the 138 or 158 or 168 hours when he does not work. They are not nearly as different from the present situation as it is different from that of the last century; and the time when we will be forced to find some sort of solution to these problems is almost certainly within the next decade or two.

On the scale of history, are we not almost there already?

Plateaus in Communication and Travel

Suppose we turn instead to the fields of communication and travel. In communication, the coming of the telephone and radio and of television in the last 20 years—now with satellite relays across the oceans—has taken us onto a plateau that is obvious to anyone who thinks about it. Once we can transmit sight and sound around the world within 2 seconds whenever we want to, there is little further to be done but to extend the networks.

It is not generally realized, however, that we are also approaching an effective plateau in our speeds of travel. I once had the idea that we ought to organize a Centenary Celebration in honor of the occasion when man first traveled faster than the top speed of any animal or bird. This important breakthrough in evolution must have occured just about 100 years ago when the steam locomotive first got up to 60 or 70 miles an hour.

Today millions of people fly at 600 miles an hour in commercial jets. Commercial supersonic transports for 2000 miles an hour are on the drawing boards; and experimental rocket planes have passed 4000 miles an hour.

How long can this acceleration of speed go on? This is an easy question to answer, because it is finished. At around 100 miles an hour, we give up land transport and take to the air. At around 17,000 miles an hour, we give up air travel because we are in orbit. And this step is already behind us.

As a matter of fact, I think the full sociological consequences of high-speed transport are already implicit in the jet-plane speeds we have today. Scarcely a hundred years ago, going around the world meant months of sailing around the Horn. Now civilians as well as armies can reach almost any point on the globe in less than a day. Can any further reduction in this time, say to 6 hours by supersonic transport, or to 1 hour by rocket, ever make as great a difference again? I think not. In most worldwide plans and operations, travel time is no longer the most significant variable.

Once horses had been tamed, men built their lives and societies around them for thousands of years. Today the United States is built around high-speed powered transportation. We have the automobile, the airplane, and the Go-Kart. It is transport that shapes the layout of roads and cities and airports and the structure and mobility of youth and workers and families and business and government. Might not our accommodations to fast easy transportation, and our attitude of taking it for granted, go on again almost unchanged for hundreds or thousands of years? I must confess that I fail to see how any new vehicle, no matter how marvelous, could again have the revolutionary effect that the railroad, the automobile, and the airplane had when they displaced the horse and carriage. Once more, regardless of future developments, in some important sense we are there already.

It is more surprising to realize that this is also almost true of space travel today, even though at the time I am writing this, it has been just 7 years since the first orbiting satellite, Sputnik, was sent up. Dramatic order-of-magnitude improvements, and manned missions to the moon and planets, and wonderful decades or centuries of exploration, are still ahead. But the moon has already been photographed from close range and the Mariner flights are under way, sending back detailed data from

Venus and Mars. Rockets already have the speed needed for exploring the solar system, and the times required would not be appreciably reduced by new plasma or nuclear rockets. The unexpected result is that the level of accessibility of the solar system that we can develop in the next 10 or 20 years may quite possibly represent its level of accessibility for hundreds of years to come.

Or to come back to terrestrial matters, consider the exploration of our own globe. Just since 1953, men have climbed the highest mountain and reached the bottom of the deepest sea. They have lived on a floating island in the Arctic and at the South Pole all year around—with running water and hot showers. Much more remains to be done, especially in exploring the oceans and penetrating the solid crust, but it is clear that the whole surface of the earth has become ours to study and use as we wish. When there is no farther to go, there is no farther to go. We have stepped up onto that plateau as well.

What about our technical achievements having to do with life and death?

I think the same imminent leveling-off can be seen here also. As everyone knows, bombs have increased in power from the 20-ton chemical "blockbuster" of the early 1940's to the 20,000-ton atomic bomb at Hiroshima and then the 20-million-ton hydrogen weapons after 1953—an increase by 6 orders of magnitude within a single decade. Today the largest hydrogen bombs are equivalent to about 100 million tons of TNT, and there are so many of them—so much "overkill"—that they could wipe out all life on the planet. But the largest ones are already too large to have maximum efficiency for surface destruction, and the use of a number of smaller ones is computed to be more "effective" for military purposes. Will we make larger bombs in the future? We can if we want to, but even for the most overwhelming military purposes, we do not need to.

Even in the matter of the *control* of nuclear weapons, I think we may be approaching some sort of limit. This takes a little explanation. How dangerous can the situation get? At the present time we are near the edge of a precipice. Every year or two there is some major international crisis where there is a serious probability of an "accident" that could trigger a nuclear war and escalate into nuclear catastrophe for the world. Korea, Suez, Berlin, Quemoy, Cuba, Vietnam. Last week's crisis, whatever it was. It is nuclear roulette, so to speak, where the probability of a fatal shot may be small each time you pull the trigger, but where, if you play the game long enough, it finally, certainly, kills you. Dedicated men have worked very hard in each of these confrontations to avoid a nuclear incident, but we may not continue to be so lucky. Next time it may be a nuclear terrorist or a suicidal maniac or just a junior officer beyond control.

As a result, some have estimated that our "half-life" under these circumstances—that is, the probable number of years before these repeated confrontations add up to a 50-50 chance of destroying the human race forever—may be only about 10 to 20 years. Obviously this is not an objectively testable number. Nevertheless the idea is clear. We see that our boasted decreases in death rates and increases in the length of individual human lives in this century are spurious, as long as this nuclear danger is so uncontrolled. This is the first time in the

history of the human race that babies—all babies everywhere forever—have had such a slim chance of survival.

Then why do I say that we are near a limit in these dangers? Just because this cannot continue. No one lives very long walking on loose rocks at the edge of a precipice. Either very soon, in 10 or 20 years, or in 30 or 40, we fall over the nuclear precipice; or else very soon, before that time runs out, we argue some sense into our collective heads and move back from the danger.

Some talk of another possibility, that we might have a nuclear war with some people still surviving—at least *this* time—by going underground, in shelters and mines. But this, even if it could work, is only a temporary and horrible postponement of the problem—like falling partway down the precipice and then getting up, battered, to fall again. Do we come out of the shelters at last, to bury and clean up and rebuild, only to have the survivors going underground again with a resurgence of nuclear powers in another 20 years or so? And then again 20 years after that? Or do we stay underground for a thousand years and hope we will mysteriously have learned how to solve the problem of our competing nuclear threats after that time?

This is obviously not an alternative at all. It is nothing but a refusal to face the necessity for agreeing eventually on a method of international nuclear control, a refusal to see that no postponement in the shelters offers anything but greater danger and difficulty.

I have gone into these alternatives here, simply to explain the basis of my conclusion that within a few years the situation will be over. Either we will be finished—or half-finished, trying to drag ourselves up again with none of the problems solved—or we will have drawn back from the precipice by actually bargaining or paying for nuclear restraints, with even the most difficult nations, so as to give us all a longer half-life.

But if in this short time ahead we can find a way to reduce these crises and probabilities by, say, a factor of 10, then we might begin to have 100 or 200 years to think how to reduce them further. And then we might begin to have a chance of lasting 2000 years —or 20,000!—hopefully, say, as long as agriculture has lasted! I can only conclude that if we live, and if we work to live, we are even now within sight of a plateau and even a falling-off in the dimension of terror. But time is running out, and it is the wisdom and effort of men today, in this present generation, within the very next few years, that will make this permanent decision for us as to whether we live or die.

Limits of Disease and Population

Finally, let us consider that other problem of life and death, the population problem.

Julian Huxley once pointed out that the two major biological inventions in historic times have been the control of germ diseases, and artificial contraceptives. They date from the work of Pasteur and of Goodyear just a hundred years ago. It is these inventions and their successors that are mainly responsible for our present population explosion—and for the hope of controlling it. They are the positive and the negative feedbacks determining human numbers.

Today bacterial diseases are approaching extinction, and virus diseases are coming under control. In the last 20 years, four of

the last great killers, malaria, syphilis, tuberculosis, and polio, have been essentially wiped out, thanks to penicillin and sulfa drugs and vaccines and DDT. Cancer and circulatory diseases remain—and let no one belittle them! But most of mankind has already acquired toward disease the Pasteurian attitude, one that we might keep for a thousand years or forever, the attitude that we can do something about disease and need not remain its helpless victims.

The trouble is that this has led to an exponential growth of population that looks overwhelming unless something is done about it. And once more we discover that this present age is the time of the transitional crisis. It is said that Paleolithic man doubled his numbers every 30,000 years. Today the world population doubles every 30 or 40 years—roughly 1000 times as fast.

This exponential growth is so steep that it cannot go on for very long, on the scale of history. Today our population is over 3 billion. By the year 2000, with a 40-year doubling time, it will be 6 billion; by 2040, 12 billion; by 2080, 25 billion; by 2120, 50 billion. This is almost 20 times our present numbers—a horrible prospect—and close to the estimated limit of the earth's food supply, even at the starvation level. But if the food supply is twice or four times as great, it is only a matter of another 40 or 80 years. The problem is in the exponential character of the growth, not in any particular numbers we put in. We see that within an uncertainty of 50 years or so, the time before the population growth slows up or levels off from starvation is only a couple of long life-times, a time no greater than the age of the United States. In fact, the famine is beginning already, with the population going up and the amount of food per capita now dropping steadily year after year in several countries.

If the world wanted to level off its population at some less extreme density before reaching universal starvation, say at a density of no more than twice our present numbers, we see that it would have to get agreements and apply effective methods of control almost immediately, for it would have to produce a leveling-off in less than 40 years. The surprising thing is that this may now be technically possible, because of the rapid development of cheaper and simpler methods of birth control, such as oral contraceptives and intrauterine coils, in the last decade. The problem is orders of magnitude easier than was believed even 5 years ago. The setting of birth rates and growth rates for a country is ceasing to be a matter of individual expense and resistance and is becoming a question rather of public policy and persuasion and effort. It is becoming a matter for conscious decision rather than collective drift. The widespread acceptance of this attitude in all countries and all religions is another plateau-step that may be taken in the very near future.

A Cultural Shock-Front

I have taken pains to enumerate these many areas where our civilization is beginning to be "past the middle of the S-curve," just because it is not generally appreciated how numerous and how central they are, or how convincing the evidence is that there are limits in sight. I realize that prediction is uncertain and that my conclusions are novel, but I think they are at least as plausible as the uncritical assumption that changes like those of the 20th century will go on forever. Marvelous developments lie

ahead, particularly in biology, but I do not think they will make as radical a change in world society, as it is now being restructured, as the changes of the last hundred years made in 19th-century social systems.

If this is true, the present generation is the hinge of history. It may be no accident that the approach to maturation in different fields shows a concurrent pattern. Our new developments in power and communication and control all support each other. And they are supporting and being supported by the simultaneous changes in economic and social and international structure. It is those aspects of technological change that have been pressing humanity so rapidly toward becoming a closely interconnected species, a species in full possession of the world and its abundance and with an adequate capacity for control and survival, that are reaching toward mature and stable forms in this generation. They are forms totally different from those of our tribal warring past, but they might conceivably go on as long as the old forms did, for hundreds or thousands of years into the future. What is happening is that we are in the midst of being compelled to reorganize the internal structure and powers of the race into a mature human integration that could be called manhood.

As a result, I think we may be now in the time of most rapid change in the whole evolution of the human race, either past or to come. It is a kind of cultural "shock-front," like the shock-fronts that occur in aerodynamics when the leading edge of an airplane wing moves faster than the speed of sound and generates the sharp pressure wave that causes the well-known sonic boom. The front edge of this pressure wave is the shock-front. It is a thin region where the low temperatures and pressures of the air ahead of the plane change suddenly to the high temperatures and pressures of the air immediately behind.

I think our present transitional crisis is a similar shock-front for the human race, buffeting us about as sudden changes in every direction come thick and fast. It is a multiple shock-front, with each type of exponential change reinforcing all the others. The Western world has encountered this cultural shock-front first—it is closer to the airplane of history, so to speak—but it would seem from the speed of industrialization of Japan and Russia that the rest of the world can be no more than 30 or 40 years behind. Throughout the world, the farm and city ways of historic man are being transformed rapidly to the ways of a high-technology world society.

Life Ahead

But the shock-front analogy is also an instructive way of thinking about the times ahead. It suggests that after the shock-front has passed, we will have reached larger powers and interactions—higher temperatures and pressures!—but that the buffeting of change will be reduced, and the times will perhaps become psychologically and socially calmer than anything this generation or this century has known.

Life will go on being different, partly for the familiar reason that we will go on having more population and power, more communication and science, in every decade. But it will also be different in a different way, because the approach to a steady state is something rare in the history of the world. We see that humanity is on the verge of a new kind of life. I think an examination of the question of what it will be

like could be one of our most constructive intellectual exercises today. It would show us how different our present problems and solutions appear, when seen in the perspective of the great changes and the different structures just ahead. It would help us see what we must do to make the changes less traumatic and to shape the structures more intelligently.

The problem of arms control, for example, becomes a different problem if it is seen as a temporary substitute for other ways of keeping the peace in a disarmed world. Innovations in education take on a different character when seen as part of the total improvement in education that will be needed for every child in the world in 50 years. The need for philosophical integration of our new knowledge about the biological and intellectual and social nature of man takes on great urgency when it is realized that this is the substructure on which the social and political philosophy of our grandchildren's world must be built. Where are our Montesquieu and Rousseau today? What have Freud and the behaviorists taught us about irrationality and educability that would help us design a good society and a free and flexible society without the danger of recurrent instability? Are many different good societies possible, and can we choose among them or move at various times from one to another?

These are problems for extensive debate, but even without answering them it is easy to show that life in any steady-state world must differ in many respects from ours.

One of the unexpected differences, for example, will be the difference in age distributions and probably a related difference in family patterns. Throughout history, children have been a majority in most societies.

The proportion of children to total population was high because so many were born who did not live to adulthood. It is estimated that at most times and places, half the population has been under age 15. Today in America, because of our postwar baby boom, half the population is still under 20. This makes a large "teen-age market" that many manufacturers are now trying to reach.

But in a steady-state world—no matter whether it has a smaller population than ours or one many times larger—the same number of people would be born in every decade and the same number would die in every decade. If our death rate in early life continues to go down, there will then be just as many people at age 40 or at age 60 as at age 10. And if they all live to about 80, as it now seems they might, then half of them will be over 40 and only one-fifth of them will be children under 15. It will be very different from the Indian village or the slum neighborhood with children everywhere underfoot. The curiosity and laughter of children will be scarce, and the world will begin to be run, even more than it has been, by the old.

A strange world, for us. But it could be a good world, if the old remain young in heart and vigor. They could use their great excess of adult-power, prosperous and leisured, to make the richest education for children that the world has ever known. Perhaps childless adults will move in with family groups, so they can share in the love and laughter of the children and spend endless hours in teaching them, in something like the old Hawaiian tradition. We may move away from our small-family separateness and back toward more tribal groupings as children become scarcer, and

as the reduction of the speed of change makes it easier for the different generations to talk to each other again.

The Quality of Life

What will we do with our time in that leisured world? Undoubtedly there will be still more travel and more vigorous and daring outdoor recreation. Life will be dull otherwise. Perhaps thousands will climb Everest and millions will ride dolphins. But I think the activities that will really begin to bloom are the creative arts and education and science. Not just Sunday painting, but Wednesday-Thursday-Friday-Saturday-Sunday painting. Continual rebuilding of your own home to your own taste, filling it with personal ingenuities and bold designs, might become the fashionable thing to do.

And education and science may become activities for everyone. Who kept up with the philosophers of the French Enlightenment? The leisured classes of the drawing rooms. Who did science, at first? Rich amateurs and leisured clerics with an easy routine and the time to do experiments. Already education and scientific research are our fastest-growing industries. With preschool enrichment raising the level of intelligence, as some evidence now indicates, perhaps increasing numbers will profit from education all the way to the graduate level, and continuing education for much of the population may become a lifelong activity.

Likewise in science, many adults may fix up a laboratory room in their houses, where they can work every day at some scientific project, some study in crystallization or in embryology or in teaching animals that could offer a lifetime of unfolding discovery.

One other characteristic of a steady-state world that deserves special mention is its requirement for a high standard of social justice. If we survive at all, after this great disturbing shock-front has faded into a phenomenon of history, it can only be by working out a new attitude of tolerance and mutual support for each other, between colored and white, between rich and poor, between advanced nations and retarded ones. The unemployed, the underprivileged, the underdeveloped, all the groups neglected or exploited by our present arrangements or condemned to exclusion from our prosperity by the accident of parentage or place of birth, form a perpetual seedbed for spokesmen and would-be dictators whose juntas may take over nuclear administration in the name of correcting these wrongs. Our failure to eradicate these evils depresses the standard of living and shortens the probable "half-life" of everyone. We are now realizing this, in Congress as well as in the councils of the world. What is fortunate for us today is that our new understanding of the educational and developmental basis of prosperity has made it possible and profitable to cure these evils just at the instant when our new weapons technology has made it absolutely necessary to do so.

We can no longer afford poverty in the world—if we ever could. We can no longer afford ignorance or prejudice or neglect. It is not so much that they are a sign of moral wickedness as that they are a sign of incompetence in design and administration. It is time to apply at least the same standards of competence and satisfaction in running the world that we apply in running a family or a business. Any member of the world now not only deserves to be shown, but must be shown, as surely as a member of a rich man's family, how he can share in its abundance. Any child in the world now not only

deserves to have education, but must have education, like a privileged child, for the full development of his potentialities from the age of one year on up. It is necessary not only because we can afford it but because we must afford it.

The world has now become too dangerous for anything less than Utopia.

New Knowledge and New Biology

Will it all be static in this strange new world of the steady state? The answer is no, nothing will be static. What will begin to be steady is our acceptance of these new ways of creative leisure and interaction as being the most interesting and most satisfying ways of life. But all our indices of flow, production, commerce, communication, will be up from what they are now. The marvelous accomplishments of a mature and integrated society will be just beginning. And two fields, scientific knowledge and biological technology, will surely go on changing and developing indefinitely.

I see no end to the increase of knowledge. When scientific research has as many men and as much money every year as society can afford, it will be adding even more rapidly than now to our knowledge of nature and to the ease with which we can control nature. And this world of nature is infinite to us, for it includes the human brain itself. After all the myriad galaxies of the astronomers are charted as well as we want to chart them, we will still go on studying the multimyriad complexities of the brain that has measured them.

Our knowledge of nature will surely be used increasingly for the improvement and variation of our biological apparatus for living. If we can actually set up a social structure that will enable us to live together without killing ourselves, for a thousand years or a million years—a time as long as the time since man began—it will begin to give us the time we need to understand and develop our full biological potentialities. Things we now cut out of the human body by surgery—the appendix, the tonsils—can they be eliminated from the hereditary genes instead? Our eyes and ears that give out when we are old, our hearts and arteries —why not make them better biologically from the beginning rather than by doctoring after they begin to fail? We begin to see the possibility of reshaping the human organism, as we have been reshaping plant and animal organisms now for many years, into a new form or into many new forms that will begin to show the full potentialities of protoplasm and the creative brain. In such a time, man will cease to be at the mercy of the evolutionary accidents that made his frame and his society—just as he has ceased to be at the mercy of the biological accidents that made his diseases. It will be a time when man can begin to plan what he wants man to be, as each individual makes his personal plans today—a time when accident and drift will finally begin to be replaced by conscious human values and decisions.

Metamorphosis

The accelerating powers and dangers and hammer-blow stresses of these days make us anxious and afraid. But I think it is clear that if we survive this shock-front, this roaring waterfall of change, we could be within sight of what Churchill once called the "sunlit uplands."

Various metaphors could be used to describe the situation. In many ways, it is like a child learning to ride a bicycle. There you were, up until that day, riding on the three-wheeler where you couldn't hurt yourself very much. But then you get the two-wheeler, and it seems terribly scary, and perhaps you fall and skin a knee or an elbow. But you get up again, and your father holds the handlebars, running along beside you, and suddenly you are riding alone. At one instant you are incompetent, falling to one side or the other and steering wrong, and the next instant it comes right and you are in control, safe and balanced not because you are fearful and slow but because you are going faster than ever. Wobbling and weaving but nevertheless choosing your *own* path and balancing safely at every turn. So, I think, in 30 or 40 years, if we survive, the human race will come through this time of wobbling conflict and uncertainty and falling, and will suddenly be riding in its own chosen direction, free, as only a coordinated and confident organism can be.

To say it another way, it is like the time of adolescence, when the teenager suddenly changes, with some thrashing about, from the dependent child to the independent man. Or it is like the moment of birth, full of pain and danger as the baby in the womb is suddenly pushed through into a new life where he must breathe alone and learn to walk and talk and think. Or it is like the moment of metamorphosis of the insect, when there is an incomprehensible swelling and dizzy changes of shape and desire in the tight cocoon, until suddenly it bursts open at the end of its own sharp S-curve, its own era of change, to reveal an unimagined transformation to a new free winged life.

This is the meaning of the leveling off of our S-curves. We are now nearing the end of the era of change. We have been isolated human beings, selfish, combative, ignorant, helpless. But now for several hundred years the great evolutionary hormones of knowledge and technology have been pressing us, almost without our understanding it, into power and prosperity and communication and interaction, and into increasing tolerance and vision and choice and planning—pressing us, whether we like it or not, into a single coordinated humankind. The scattered and competing parts are being bound together. Everywhere now we begin to see men and nations beginning the deliberate design of development with a growing confidence in the choice and creation of their own future. The exponential changes have burst apart our ancient attitudes and structures, and our failure to adjust to this may yet kill us, but if we are wise and energetic and understand our own nature and purposes well enough to restructure and control these dangers, mankind may emerge very quickly into coordinated forms such as it has never known. Our drastic changes will not go on forever. They are converging to a limit. It was implicit in the biological material all along, as surely as the butterfly is implicit in the caterpillar. We have been men. We are emerging into Man.

Yet no analogy, not even that of metamorphosis, quite captures the suddenness and radicalness, the really complete restructuring, of the transformation ahead. If the 2 billion years of life are represented by the 200-foot height of, say, the Rockefeller Chapel at Chicago, the million years of man make a 1-inch block on top of the chapel. The 20,000 years of agriculture make a thick postage stamp on top of that, and the 400 years of science make the ink on top of the postage stamp. Now, suddenly, we see what all this has been building up to; and it is about to come within a single generation or two—that is, in the thickness of the film of moisture on top of the ink on the postage stamp. In that short time we will move, if we survive the strain, to a wealthy and powerful and coordinated world society reaching across the solar system, a society that might find out how to keep itself alive and evolving for thousands or millions or billions of years, a time as long as all of evolution past. It is a tremendous prospect. Hardly anyone has seen the enormous sweep and restructuring and unity and future of it except perhaps dreamers like H. G. Wells or Teilhard de Chardin. It is a quantum jump. It is a new state of matter. The act of saving ourselves, if it succeeds, will make us participants in the most incredible event in evolution. It is the step to Man.